Handbook
for Metric
Conversion

First Printing December 1973
Printed in the United States of America

Published by Idaho Research Foundation, Inc., University Station Box 3367, Moscow, Idaho 83843

Handbook
for Metric
Conversion

By

Dale M. Johnson
The University of Tulsa

and

Bob M. VanOsdol
The University of Tulsa

Contents

"Weights and Measures may be ranked among the necessaries of life to every individual of human society. They enter into the economical arrangements and daily concerns of every family. They are necessary to every occupation of human industry; to the distribution and security of every species of property; to every transaction of trade and commerce; to the labors of the husbandmen; to the ingenuity of artificer; to the studies of the philosopher; to the researches of the antiquarian; to the navigation of the mariner and the marches of the soldier; to the exchanges of peace and all the operations of war"

John Quincy Adams

PREFACE

In 1875, the United States essentially endorsed the metric system of measures by being one of the original signatories of the "Treaty of Meter" in Paris. About two decades later in 1894, the United States became officially a metric nation when the Secretary of Treasury declared the new metric standards to be the nation's "fundamental standards" of length and mass. Although conversion to the metric system has been discussed and debated for over a hundred years in the United States, relatively little headway has been made toward its implementation. Since World War II, over 40 bills aimed at achieving a general conversion have been introduced, but without much effect. In the early 1970's two observations became apparent. The first was that Congress would pass legislation that would bring about the conversion. Secondly, with or without congressional action, conversion to the metric system was inevitable and would eventually be a reality in the U.S.

Presently, debate over whether we will or should live in a metric society is *nihil ad rem* and incidental. Discussion of the pros and cons of conversion may enhance public understanding and awareness, but it is apparent that the U.S. will literally join the rest of the world on weights and measures—and probably the sooner, the better. Already drug measurement, electrical quantities, film width, snow ski length, and other manufactured goods utilize the metric system. Recently published cook books, for example, give measures in both customary terms (cups, ounces, tablespoons, etc.) as well as metric unit equivalents.

This book is an attempt by the authors to provide the general public with a nontechnical discussion of measurements and more specifically to relate the metric system and conversion to already familiar concepts. It provides essential information for conversion and comparison of units of measurement, weights, and temperature scales between the metric system and other systems which have been in common use in the United States. Although several measurement systems have been utilized in theU.S., for the purpose of this manual, these are grouped and called the "English" system for reference purposes. This may not be an entirely accurate labeling, but within context no confusion will develop since systems other than the metric system will be "English".

The manual is intended to serve as a self-instruction text for anyone who wishes to familiarize himself or herself with metric-English system conversion. No specialized knowledge is assumed beyond being able to multiply and divide decimal numbers.

USE OF THE PROGRAMMED TEXT

This text has been designed to yield clarity and understanding if used in the intended method. The reader will find that mastery of a particular chapter will be enhanced by first reading the Introduction. Following the Introduction, each chapter is a self-contained unit and understanding is not dependent upon other chapters, although a good deal of generalization in methods can be made throughout the text.

A programmed text is a self-instruction text. This simply means that the reader will find small units of information presented followed by some reader activity that will reinforce the concept presented. Thus, each chapter should be read and questions answered from the first of the chapter to the end of the chapter, since the progression will build throughout.

The following steps are suggested for study:
1) Read the information presented.
2) Answer the question .
3) Check the solution which immediately follows the question.
4a) If you answer correctly, continue with the next step.
4b) If you answer incorrectly, study the solution before continuing.

NOTE: On occasion, there may be several *different* methods of working a problem; however, there will be *only one* correct answer when rounded off to the same number of places. Only one method of working the problem will be presented in the solution section.

1 INTRODUCTION

What Is Measurement?

Measurement in its broadest context may be defined as a process of assigning numerical values (numbers) to properties, attributes, or definable characteristics of events or objects according to some scaling scheme. By and large, we think of measurement as a process which tells us "how much" of an attribute or characteristic is present. Thus, we describe a 240 pound guard on a football team, a 6'11" forward on a basketball team, an acre of land, a bushel of wheat, or a pint of cream. We fret over a forecast for a high temperature for a winter day of 28° Fahrenheit, marvel over a 9.3 second 100 yard dash, and are pleased with a positive bank balance at the end of the month. Such properties are measurable and the various sizes or magnitudes are comparable within the appropriate system of units. In other words, we can directly compare an age of 16 years and an age of 42 years or any two measurements within the same "system". It makes less sense to compare weight of 130 pounds with an I.Q. score of 120 points because the attributes under consideration are different characteristics.

Thus, the first step in the measurement of a property is the selection of a convenient unit of measure. After the unit is selected, it follows then that any measurement may be made in terms of multiples of that unit, or fractional parts of that unit. For example, one familiar unit is the "inch". A shirt collar size may be 16 inches, or 16 times the one-inch unit.

The history of unit selection for most of our common measurements is quite fascinating. Early units were selected by quite natural methods. To illustrate, originally the foot was the actual length of a human foot. However, before it was standardized, it ranged in size from 9 inches to 19 inches—not a very consistent selection. Henry I of

England, during the twelfth century, decreed the lawful yard to be the distance from the end of his thumb as his arm was held horizontally to the end of his nose. Two centuries later, Edward II defined the inch as the end to end length of three barley corns that were taken from the center of the ear. After another two centuries, the lawful rod was established to be the combined length of the left feet of sixteen Englishmen lined up in a row as they left church. Also during the sixteenth century, Henry VIII defined the pound to be the weight of 7,000 grains of well dried wheat taken from the middle of the ear. The first known measurement of length was the cubit (approximately 20 inches) which was the distance from the elbow point to the end of the middle finger.

It is evident that the early units of measurement were unreliable and loosely defined. Because of this indefinite quality of units, confusion and measurement error were the rule rather than the exception.

With the advancement of civilization and the development of international trade, a standardization of units was required. Today, relatively ideal standard units for everyday measurement problems exist in fairly invariable forms. Many basic units have been standardized to correspond very close to the defined units on display at the International Bureau of Weights and Measures. Although the standardization process has led to more reliable measurements, the units of measurement are still quite arbitrary and artificial.

What Are Measuring Systems?

There exist several systems of weights and measures with which we are familiar as well as systems with which most of us are only vaguely acquainted. For instance, feet for measuring distance, square yards for measuring area, cubic inches for volume, bushels for capacity (roughly speaking, another way of saying volume), and pounds for weight are relatively common measures with which we have daily contact. However, there are systems that are less frequently encountered. In the Avoirdupois system, 16 ounces is equivalent to one pound; in the Troy system, 12 ounces equals one pound; and in the Apothecaries system, 96 drams is one pound. Surveyors frequently utilize less common terms for measures of length such as link, rod, or chain. Similarly, maritime distances are defined in terms of fathoms, cable lengths, nautical miles, and leagues. Consequently, if a fixed

2

distance between two points were to be measured, we could express that distance in one of several systems. The distance would not change, but we might express that distance in many ways. In one system, we might find that the distance was 2 feet; in another system, the same distance would be expressed as about 61 centimeters; while in another system, the length would be approximately 3 links, and so on. The point is that the distance is constant, but the units of measure changes from system to system. The same discussion could be applied to area, volume, weight, temperature, and other measurable properties.

Having made the point that measuring units vary from system to system, it may somewhat undramatically be stated now that the metric system is simply another system for expressing length, area, volume, weight, and temperature. Why then, is the metric system drawing so much attention? If it is just another system for accomplishing the same purposes that other schemes do, why add to the confusion? These are typical questions that must be answered before justification for its existence can be demonstrated. However, before explicitly attempting to answer these queries, let's take a closer look at this scheme of metric measures.

What Is the Metric System?

The basic unit of length in the metric system, the meter, will serve as a launching point for our discussion. At the beginning of the 19th century, the French government attempted to devise an ideal unit of length. This fundamental unit was called a meter and was defined to be $1/10,000,000$ (one-tenmillionth) of the distance from the earth's equator to one pole. By utilizing elaborate and costly survey results, the standard meter was constructed. Unfortunately, survey equipment was not sophisticated enough at that time to allow for the accuracy needed. Errors crept into the calculations, and later it was discovered that the meter as defined really had no relation to the distance from the equator to a pole. The attempt did have merit although the length of one meter is now recognized as an arbitrary distance. The meter, technically defined, is the distance at the temperature of melting ice between the centers of two lines traced on the platinum-iridium bar deposited at the International Bureau of Weights and Measures. For most of our needs, the meter may be thought of as a distance of about 39⅓ inches for reference purposes.

The gram is the basic unit of weight in the metric system. Imagine, if you will, that you have broken the meter into one-hundred equal lengths. Each of these smaller units of length is called a centimeter. Now visualize a box (cube) with dimensions of one centimeter long, one centimeter wide, and one centimeter high. This cube is called a cubic centimeter. How does this relate to weight? Well, consider the weight of one cubic centimeter of distilled water. That's one gram of weight (or mass). Finally, by combining one-thousand of these cubic centimeters, we arrive at the basic metric unit of volume—the liter (pronounced "leeter" and sometimes spelled "litre"). For reference, the liter is just over a liquid quart; that is, 1 liter = 1.057 liquid quarts. These basic units will be discussed in detail in subsequent chapters.

Thus far, nothing has been revealed that would answer the question posed earlier—why introduce just another system of measurement when several already exist? The straightforward and oversimplified answer is that of all systems of measurement in common use, the metric system is the most logical from the standpoint of notational development and use, not to mention economic advantages discussed later. The reader should not be misled at this point. Surely there is nothing more "logical" about a meter than a yard. There is no magic to the amount of weight of a gram above and beyond the ounce or pound. And there is nothing superior about a liter when compared to a quart. So, what then prompts such a statement as the metric system is more logical? The decimalization notation and consistency of the system is the key. Throughout this booklet, the reader will be struck by the feeling that "I've seen this before". Indeed, the consistency of the metric system across measures and weights should leave you in complete command of the system if you "get the hang" of the terminology.

The first set of terms with which to become familiar is the prefixes used in the metric system. Some of the more common prefixes are presented in Table 1. For now, do not be concerned with units, but only with prefixes to units. The unit may be a unit of length (distance), area, volume, or weight; it doesn't matter.

Notice in Table 1 that the prefixes actually designate what the unit has been multiplied by. "Centi" means that the unit has been multiplied by 1/100, or stated another way, the unit has been divided by 100. Remember how the centimeter was determined previously—the meter was divided into 100 equal lengths, each of the divisions was a

centimeter. With the coming of the Atomic Age, the public became familiar with the term **mega**ton which means a *million* tons, or one ton multiplied by 1,000,000. From viewing the Olympic Games, the **kilo**meter became a household word meaning 1,000 meters. So, many of these prefixes represent a well known concept. Check yourself; what would a **deka**meter represent in terms of meters? Or a **deka**gram in terms of weight? Or a **deka**liter in volume? In each case, it would represent 10 of the particular units.

The complete set of prefixes provides for each multiple of ten, or one-tenth of a unit. In more concise terms, the metric system not only coordinates the measurements of length, area, volume, and weight, but also provides a convenient decimalized system for each type of measure. Thus, the metric system was conceived as a measurement system to the base ten; that is, the units of the system, their multiples, and submultiples are related to each other by simple factors of ten just as pennies, dimes, and dollars. This enhances the convenience of the system because it is congruent with our system for counting and

---

TABLE 1 **METRIC PREFIXES**

Multiplication Factor	Prefix
1,000,000	mega
1,000	kilo
100	hecto
10	deka
1	(unit)
$.1 = \frac{1}{10}$	deci
$.01 = \frac{1}{100}$	centi
$.001 = \frac{1}{1000}$	milli
$.000001 = \frac{1}{1,000,000}$	micro

---

numerical notation which is also a base ten system. To convert between units, their multiples and submultiples, it is not necessary to perform lengthy multiplication or division operations, but simply shift the decimal point to the right if multiplying and to the left if dividing. More will be said about this convenient feature of the metric system subsequently. However, for contrast at this point, stop and think about conversion within the system we presently use. To convert feet to inches, multiply by a factor of 12. To change feet to yards, divide by a factor of 3. To figure the number of feet in 25 miles, multiply 25 by 5,280. Consider the difficulty of remembering the conversion factors for converting cups to pints, pecks to bushels, drams to scruples, teaspoons to cups, square rods to acres, and gallons to hogsheads—not to mention grains to pennyweight, skeins to yards, and so on. Quite a confusing situation when you think of it. In addition, we have to avoid certain ambiguous situations that arise in present systems. Does 8 quarts equal 1 peck, or does 8 quarts equal 2 gallons? The answer is both; however, it depends on whether you are thinking in terms of dry or liquid measure. Does 16 ounces equal one pound, or one pint? The answer again is—both. But how can both be correct? Because the former is weight scaled in the Avoirdupois system and the latter is a measure of volume in the Apothecaries liquid system.

In summary then, the ambiguity and confusion are for the most part eliminated by utilizing a single system. Moreover, the problem of intersystem conversion virtually vanishes with the metric system because every unit is a multiple of some power of ten. Since over 90% of the countries of the world are currently using the metric system, international trade, travel, and communication will be enhanced by a U.S. conversion to the metric system.

Why Convert?

The reader who is not familiar with the metric system of weights and measures is undoubtedly not convinced that the trouble, expense, and inconvenience of changing to the metric system would be justified in terms of positive outcomes. After all, a Miss America with measurements of 98-60-98 would certainly be received with a good deal of astonishment to those not acquainted with the magnitude of the length of a centimeter. Housewives buying fabric by the meter, milk by the liter, and bacon by the gram is not commonplace by any means on the American market scene. Motorists measuring distance in kilometers, medical doctors announcing that a patient's temperature is normal at 36.9 degrees, or a land promoter advertising land for sale in hectare units are concepts foreign to Americans. These units of measures are hardly part of our everyday vocabulary.

Actually, when one considers the entire world's population, the metric units are quite in style, as only a small minority of the earth's people use the English system. Australia, Canada, Great Britain, Japan, and the United States are the only major powers that are not on the metric system. Presently, each of these nations is moving toward a conversion. Other countries in which the metric system is not used include Barbados, Burma, Gambia, Ghana, Jamaica, Liberia, Malaui, Muscat and Oman, Nauru, Sierra Leone, Southern Yema, Tonga, and Trinidad. Approximately 90 percent of the world's people use the metric system, and this percentage is increasing yearly.

Plans have been formulated to implement a complete changeover to a metric America over a ten year period. This changeover period really refers to the length of time for the U.S. to become predominantly, but not exclusively, metric. Some things would change rapidly, others would change more slowly, and some will probably not change. In the majority of the cases, metric items would replace obsolete or worn out articles. That is, when a housewife dropped her conventional measuring cup on a tile floor, she would replace it with a new metric model. This would be the case with most manufacturing businesses and industries as well as households and other places where conversions of hardware is concerned.

On the other hand, we'll not have to rewrite the song "I Love You a Bushel and A Peck" nor replace all of the football artificial turf with metric units. In cooking, a pinch will still be a pinch, a smattering will still be a smattering, a sprig will remain a sprig, a slice will be a slice, and one medium onion will be one medium onion forever, although 7½ cups will undoubtedly be changed to 1.7 liters.

As pointed out earlier, the question of whether the U.S. should convert to the metric system is moot and even beside the point. Most of us are aware that the conversion will be troublesome and expensive—anything is that is done on a national level. Some advantages of the metric system other than "it's nice to work with" seem in order. Some of these are outlined below.

1. It would facilitate and encourage trade and commerce resulting

in increased exports for the U.S.

2. The consumer would benefit as price comparisons would be greatly simplified due to the easily comparable units of weights, measure, and volume.

3. Communication would be vastly improved since one system would be adopted and used.

4. Much, if not all, of the cost of conversion will be made up simply by being on the metric system. For instance, manufacturers presently must concern themselves with dual dimensioning (e.g. inches and centimeters) on blueprints and engineering drawings.

5. Since the majority of our scientific and technical material already utilizes the metric units, duplication will be eliminated and our scientific community and public will be on the same system.

6. The metric system is well tested and has passed every test with flying colors. It is impressive that not a single nation which has adopted the metric system has ever abandoned it.

This is only a beginning of the list of advantages and is in no way meant to be complete. The six points are only illustrative of the factors which have combined to outweigh the problems associated with conversion. So, as one could predict, the public will be learning and thinking in metric units almost exclusively within the next ten years.

Units of Measurement

Linear Measure. The popular notion of length is synonymous with the term linear measure. It is simply the answer to "how far?" in terms of distance between two points. We have relatively convenient units of linear measure—inches, feet, yards, rods, miles, light-years, etc. Appropriate units are selected for descriptive purposes. For example, inches are convenient for designating the distance around a shirt collar; feet are more convenient for measuring the height of a pole vault; and yards are more suitable for longer distances such as the length of a football field. Inches could be used to describe the distance from New York City to Washington, D.C., but units of miles are more appropriate for such distances. Even though these familiar units are fairly well suited for describing distances, conversion from one unit to another in our customary English system is rather awkward. For instance, changing feet to inches and inches to yards have very little in common as far as conversion factors are concerned; not to mention feet to chains, miles to rods, and yards to miles. There is little consistency.

Within the metric system, the conversion is considerably easier. We'll discuss this in depth in Chapter 2. As mentioned earlier, the basic metric unit of length is the meter, and subdivisions of the meter which are commonly used for shorter distances are the centimeter (one-hundredth of a meter) and the millimeter (one-thousandths of a meter). Again, the meter is just over a yard long and a centimeter is roughly one-third of an inch. For longer distances, the kilometer (or 1000 meters) is an appropriate metric unit of length.

Area. Closely related to linear units are units of area or square units. Whereas linear units are used to measure length and width for example, square units designate area. More specifically, feet and yards are used for linear measure; square feet and square yards are used to measure area. Area then, is a two-dimensional concept while distance or linear measure is in one dimension.

Common measures of area in the metric system are square centimeters, square meters, square kilometers, the are, and the hectare. Area conversions are discussed in Chapter 3.

Volume and Capacity. Volume and capacity are three-dimensional concepts. That is to say, measurements of volume imply that the object has length, width, and height. Usually, volume refers to how much space is occupied by the object. On the other hand, capacity has reference to how much will a container hold. A refrigerator occupies space in a kitchen. Also, it has capacity for containing say 15 cubic feet of food. Both volume and capacity may be measured in cubic units.

Units of length are used to define volume or capacity. In fact, units of length in three dimension are used and these measurements are called cubic units. We usually think of cubic feet or cubic yards for capacity or volume. The notion of capacity carries through to liquid measure. For instance, a cup of water, a tablespoon of honey, or a quart of milk are familiar measures of liquid. Metric cubic units are discussed further in Chapter 4. These include cubic centimeter, cubic millimeter, liter, cubic meter, and others.

Weight. Weight may be defined as the force of gravity on an object. Unlike the previously discussed measurements, weight is not necessarily determined by its physical size. A large balloon filled with hot air may not register on a set of scales, while a small cube of lead may weigh several pounds.

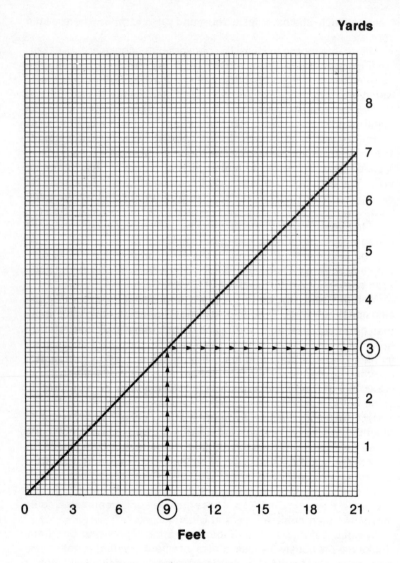

Figure 1 **Feet - Yards Conversion**

The basic unit of weight in the metric system is the gram. However, the kilogram (or 1000 grams) is probably more useful for most of us. Units of weight are discussed in Chapter 5.

Temperature. Although the metric system does not include a special temperature scale, the centigrade or Celsius scale is used in every country which utilizes the metric system of weights and measures. The freezing point of water on the Celsius scale is 0° and the boiling point of water is 100°. This scale has been preferred in the scientific community and will undoubtedly have expanded use and application in our metric society as the changeover takes place. Chapter 6 is devoted to temperature conversion.

Graphic Representation

Throughout the text, two basic methods of conversion are discussed. One method approaches conversion with the use of a formula and a conversion factor or constant multiplier. The second method uses a graphic approach. Generally, the former method is more accurate and the latter method is easier and quicker if an estimate will suffice. It is the graphic method that is illustrated in this section to aid the reader in interpreting the graphs in the pages that follow.

For converting one unit to another via a graph, several terms or graph parts must be identified. Each graph has two axes—one representing each unit. The two axes are perpendicular to each other and are labeled with the corresponding units.

To read the graph, follow these steps:

1) Locate the unit that you want to change on the appropriate axis.

2) Move up (or horizontally) until you intersect the straight line graph.

3) Move across horizontally (or down) until you intersect the other axis.

4) The point at which you intersected the second axis in Step 3 is the conversion answer.

For illustration purposes, Figure 1 is a graphical representation of the conversion of feet to yards and vice versa.

To change 9 feet to "x" yards, follow the steps:

1) Locate 9 feet on the horizontal axis.

2) Move straight up from that point to the graph.

3) Move across and intersect the vertical axis.

4) Note that the answer is 3 yards which is read directly from the axis.

Notice that by using Figure 1, you can also convert yards to feet by selecting the unit in yards, moving horizontally to the line graph, then moving down to the answer in feet. Try several to get the feel of using the graph before continuing.

At this point, it would be well to re-read the section just prior to the Introduction entitled "Use of the Programmed Text" before proceeding through the remaining chapters.

2 MEASUREMENTS OF LENGTH

Metric to English Conversion

In this section, we will concern ourselves with the conversion of metric measures of length to English equivalents. The term equivalent here means that at most two or three decimal place accuracy will serve all but scientific purposes, where more precision may be required. The general scheme in this section is to progress from shorter measurements to the longer distance measurements that are used in our everyday affairs. Linear measurement, length, and distance are used to describe the same quality—namely, to describe how far it is from one point to another.

For practical use in our daily activities, common metric units of length are the millimeter (mm) and the centimeter (cm). For the expression of these smaller dimensions, we have been accustomed to using fractions of an inch or inches. The conversion of centimeters to inches is given in Formula 2.1

(2.1)   Centimeters × 0.39 = Inches

Formula 2.1 may be interpreted this way: a quantity of centimeters multiplied by the constant 0.39 will yield a quantity of inches. For example, 50 centimeters when converted to inches would result in 50 × 0.39 = 19.5 or 19½ inches. Remember, when multiplying by a decimal fraction, the number of decimal places in the answer is the same as the total number in the two numbers that are multiplied together.

Problem 2.1   If two numbers are multiplied together and one of the numbers has one decimal place and the other has two decimals such as 3.5 and 6.25, how many places will be marked off in the answer?

Solution 2.1   **Three** because 3.**5** has one decimal place and 6.**25** has two decimal places and $1 + 2 = 3$.

The reader should be reminded that the accuracy is not necessarily to three decimal places in the above example. However, we usually round our answers off to whatever is practical for the situation under consideration.

Problem 2.2   Using Formula 2.1, convert 60 centimeters to inches.

Solution 2.2   **23.4 inches**

$$\begin{array}{r} 60 \\ \times .39 \\ \hline 540 \\ 180 \\ \hline 23.40 \end{array}$$

$60 \times 0.39 = 23.4$ inches

Problem 2.3   *The diameter of a 33⅓ rpm record disk is about 30 cm., what is the diameter in inches?*

Solution 2.3   **11.7 inches**

$$\begin{array}{r} 30 \\ \times .39 \\ \hline 270 \\ 90 \\ \hline 11.70 \end{array} = 11.7 \text{ inches}$$

Problem 2.4   Remembering that the number of decimal places in the answer is the sum of the decimals in the two numbers being multiplied, how many inches are equal to 48.5 cm?

Solution 2.4   **18.915 inches**   48.5 cm
                                        ×.39
                                        ─────
                                        4365
                                        1455
                                        ─────
                                        18.915 inches

(Note: we might want to round off to 18.92, 18.9, or 19 inches depending on our needs.)

Problem 2.5   One cm = _____ inches.

Solution 2.5   **0.39 inches**   1 × 0.39 = 0.39 inches

Millimeters (mm) are commonly used for expressing very small distances. To convert millimeters to inches, use the conversion factor 0.039 as shown in Formula 2.2

(2.2)   millimeters × 0.039 = inches

For example, 200 mm represents the same distance as 7.8 inches and the conversion is made by the use of Formula 2.2 this way:

                        200 mm
                        × .039
                        ──────
                        1800
                        600
                        ──────
                        7.800 inches

Problem 2.6   Change 500 mm to inches

Solution 2.6   *19.5 inches*   500 mm
                                     × .039
                                     ──────
                                     4500
                                     1500
                                     000
                                     ──────
                                     19.500 inches

Problem 2.7   The width of common notebook paper is about 219 millimeters. What is the approximate width in inches?

Solution 2.7   **8.5 inches** $219 \times .039 = 8.541$ inches

---

Problem 2.8   To change millimeters to inches, multiply the number of mm's by the constant _____.

Solution 2.8   **.039**, see Formula 2.2

Whereas feet and yards in the English system have been common units for expressing intermediate lengths, the meter is the analogous unit in the metric system. The three formulas given below show the conversion factors for converting meters to inches, feet, and yards respectively.

(2.3)   **meters × 39.37 = inches**
(2.4)   **meters × 3.28 = feet**
(2.5)   **meters × 1.09 = yards**

Problem 2.9   To convert meters to inches, multiply the number of meters by the constant_____.

Solution 2.9   **39.37** see Formula 2.3

Problem 2.10   How many inches are equivalent to 2.5 meters?

Solution 2.10   **98.425 inches** $2.5 \times 39.37 = 98.425$

Problem 2.11   In the 1972 Olympic Games, the 200 meter dash

16

was won with a time of 20 seconds. Convert this distance to a) feet, and b) yards.

Solution 2.11   a) **656 feet**   200 × 3.28 = 656.00
                   b) **218 yards**   200 × 1.09 = 218.00

Longer distances such as how far it is from one city to another are expressed in kilometers (km) in the metric system. For reference purposes, the kilometer is 1000 meters, or 1094 yards, or just less than two-thirds of a mile. Formula 2.6 shows the conversion method for changing km to miles.

$$\textbf{(2.6)} \quad \textbf{kilometers} \times \textbf{0.62} = \textbf{miles}$$

Problem 2.12   Convert 300 km to miles.

Solution 2.12   **186 miles**   300 × .62 = 186.00

Problem 2.13   If an automobile is traveling 50 km per hour, this speed would be _____ miles per hour.

Solution 2.13   **31 miles per hour**   50 × .62 = 31.00

(This problem reduces to one of changing km to miles since speed is the *distance* traveled in one hour.)

English to Metric Conversion

In this section, methods for converting inches to millimeters and centimeters, feet to meters, yards to meters, and miles to kilometers are discussed. This may appear quite similar to the previous section; however, the converse of the previous section is the topic of concern now. In other words, we are changing English units of linear measure to approximate metric units. Actually, given the conversion factors, one can convert either way—metric to English or vice versa—by ratio and proportion or by graphical methods. However, considering the conversion factors in separate sections, we can simply concern ourselves with a conversion factor and one arithmetic process—that of multiplication.

Formulas 2.7 and 2.8 are for converting inches to millimeters and centimeters respectively.

(2.7)   Inches × 25.4 = millimeters
(2.8)   Inches × 2.54 = centimeters

If we wish to convert one foot to both millimeters (mm) and centimeters (cm), we would simply multiply 12 (since 12 inches = 1 foot) by 25.4 and 2.54 to get the solutions.

That is: 12 inches × 25.4 = 304.8 mm and
                    12 inches × 2.54 = 30.48 cm.

Problem 2.14   How long is a yard stick in terms of mm and cm?

Solution 2.14   **914.4 mm**   36 in × 25.4 = 914.4 mm
                  91.44 cm   36 in × 2.54 = 91.44 cm

To convert feet to meters (m), use the multiplier constant in Formula 2.9

(2.9)   Feet × .305 = meters

Further, to convert yards to meters, use Formula 2.10.

(2.10)   Yards × .91 = meters

As can be seen from the formulas, a meter is a little longer than a yard and a foot is just less than a third of a meter.

Problem 2.15   Convert 90 feet to meters.

Solution 2.15   **27.45 meters**   90 × .305 = 27.450

Problem 2.16   If the length of a football field (100 yards) were
                   measured in metric units, how many meters long
                   would it be?

Solution 2.16   **91 meters**   100 yds. × .91 = 91.00

Formula 2.11 can be used to change miles to kilometers.

     (2.11)   miles × 1.61 = kilometers

Problem 2.17   The distance from San Francisco, California to
                   Mobile, Alabama is 2400 miles. How many
                   kilometers would express this distance?

Solution 2.17   **3864 km**   2400 × 1.61 =3864.00 km

Graphic Representation

If you are unfamiliar with interpreting straight line graphs, return
to Chapter 1 and reread the section on Graphic Representation. The
four graphs in this section allow relatively rapid conversion from one
system to another. The conversion by graphs have basically two
limitations. First, the conversions are generally estimates or interpo-
lations and thus are approximations. Secondly, the range of units are
necessarily limited by space and consequently large number conversion is impractical. On the other hand, both English to metric and
metric to English transformations can be made on the same graph.
Figure 2 may be used for inch-centimeter conversion. Figures 3, 4,
and 5 are conversions for feet-meters, yards-meters, and miles-
kilometers respectively.

In Figure 2, each unit on the horizontal unit on the graph represents ½ inch and each vertical unit on the "up and down" axis
represents one centimeter. Thus to change 20 inches to centimeters,
we find 20 inches on the horizontal axis, move *up* to the line graph,
then move across horizontally to the centimeter axis which is just less
than 51 centimeters.

Centimeters

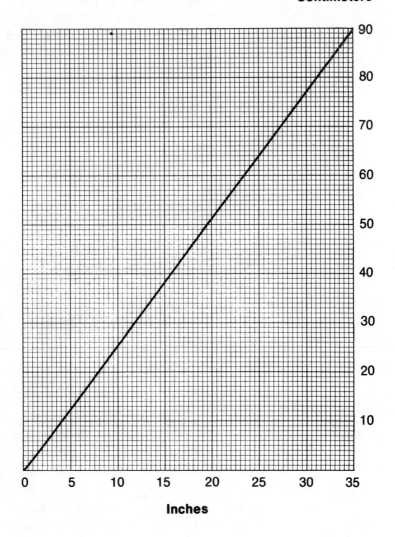

Inches

Figure 2 **Inch - Centimeter Conversion**

Problem 2.18   About _____ cm is equal to 15 inches.

Solution 2.18   **38 cm** (The graph at 15 inches is 8 units above the 30 on the cm axis.)

By reversing the process, centimeters can be converted to inches. You can locate 38 cm on the vertical axis and move left to the line graph and then down to 15 inches. This would verify the Solution 2.18.

Problem 2.19   52 cm = _____ in.

Solution 2.19   **20.5 inches** (Since each unit on the inch axis represents .5 inches, the graph value at one unit to the right of 20 would be 20.5).

Figure 3 shows a Feet-Meter conversion graph. Each unit on the horizontal (feet) axis represents one foot whereas each small unit on the vertical axis represents 0.2 of a meter, or each large unit (10 of the smaller units) represents 2 meters.

Problem 2.20   20 feet = _____ meters

Solution 2.20   **6 meters**

Problem 2.21   8.2 meters = _____ feet

Solution 2.21   **27 feet.** 8.2 m is one small unit above 8m and that corresponds to about 27 on the horizontal axis.

Figure 4 is interpreted in a similar fashion. Units on the horizontal (yards) axis represent one yard and vertical (meters) units represent one meter.

Meters

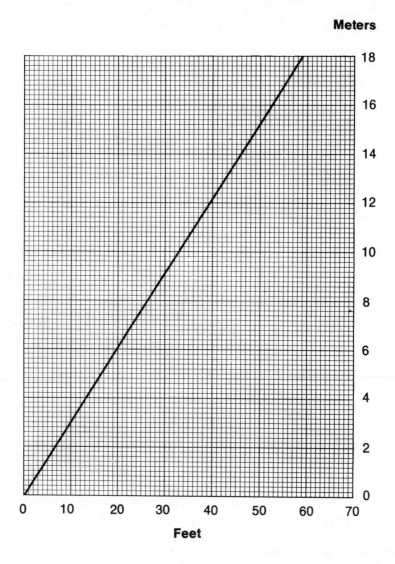

Feet

Figure 3 **Feet - Meter Conversion**

Meters

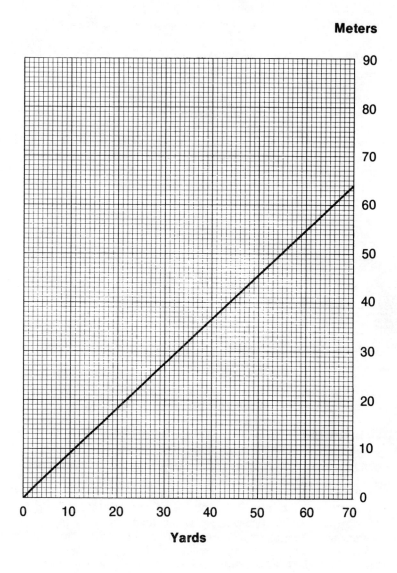

Yards

Figure 4 **Yard - Meter Conversion**

Problem 2.22   Change 50 meters to yards using Figure 4

Solution 2.22   about **55 yards**

Keep in mind that the results from the graphs are approximate and are appropriate for quick reference if estimates are desired. Formulas are also not exact in most cases. However the use of the formulas and conversion factors are more accurate generally than the graphs. At times, you may want to refer back to the previous sections and compare your computational results to the results obtained from the graphs to get an idea of how much error is introduced in your interpretation of the graph.

The horizontal axis units in Figure 5 represent one mile and vertical units represent one kilometer.

Problem 2.23   A distance of 37 miles when converted to km via Figure 5 would be _____ kilometers.

Solution 2.23   **60 km** (approx.)

Metric to Metric Conversion

The preceding sections have dealt with the conversion from one system of linear measure to another system. Eventually this will be unnecessary as metric units will become commonplace enough that we will be as familiar with them as we are the conventional English units now. In fact, some advocate that a discussion of relations between the two systems is not desirable because the metric system should be learned and used without reference to the English system units. While this approach has merit and advantages, the authors' position is that this approach is unrealistic in light of practical situations that will confront members of our society during the changeover period, because we will indeed still be using a dual system and comparisons will need to be made. With that idea in mind as the rationale for the previous sections, we'll now turn our attention exclusively to metric linear measures in this section.

The basic unit of length in the metric system is the meter (m). All other metric units of length are derived from the meter. That is, other

Kilometers

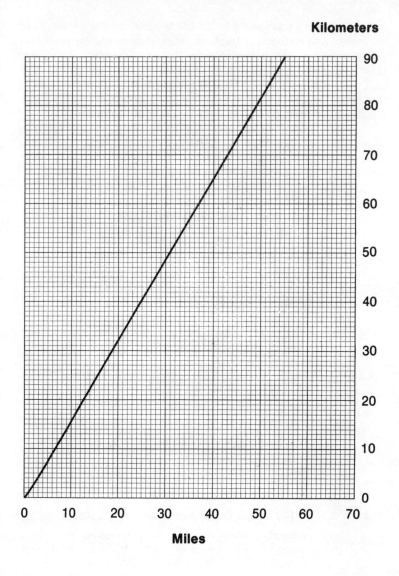

Miles

Figure 5 **Mile - Kilometer Conversion**

units are either a fractional portion of the meter or else a multiple of the meter. And further, the fractional subdivisions and the multiples are all powers of ten—the same as our system of counting. This has at least a couple of implications: 1) common fractions are for the most part replaced by decimal fractions similar to our notation of dollars and cents, and 2) conversion from one unit to another is considerably simplified when compared to conversion in our English system.

The term "meter" is included in all of the units. The difference in terminology is only in the prefix to "meter". Consequently, it would be advantageous to have some practice using the prefixes. Table 1 from Chapter 1 is repeated here for convenience.

TABLE 1 **METRIC PREFIXES**

Multiplication Factor	Prefix
1,000,000	mega
1,000	kilo
100	hecto
10	deka
1	(unit)
$.1 = {}^1/_{10}$	deci
$.01 = {}^1/_{100}$	centi
$.001 = {}^1/_{1000}$	milli
$.000001 = {}^1/_{1,000,000}$	micro

Problem 2.24   100 meters in the metric system is called a _____.

Solution 2.24   **hectometer** 100 meters is 100 times the basic unit as shown in Table 1.

Problem 2.25   If a meter were divided into one-thousand equal
parts, each portion would be a _____?

Solution 2.25   **millimeter** one-thousandths of a meter.

Notice also from Table 1 that adjacent prefixes are multiples of 10
with respect to each other. For example, Table 2 shows this relationship between the various units. A millimeter, for instance, is $^1/_{10}$ of a
centimeter; a centimeter is $^1/_{10}$ of a decimeter; and so on.

TABLE 2 **RELATIONSHIPS BETWEEN METRIC LINEAR UNITS**

1 **millimeter** = $^1/_{10}$ centimeter	= $^1/_{100}$ decimeter	$\doteq$ $^1/_{1000}$ meter
10 millimeters = **1 centimeter**	= $^1/_{10}$ decimeter	= $^1/_{100}$ meter
100 millimeters = 10 centimeters =	**1 decimeter**	= $^1/_{10}$ meter
1000 millimeters = 100 centimeters =	10 decimeters =	**1 meter**

---

1 **meter** = $^1/_{10}$ dekameter	= $^1/_{1000}$ hectometer	=$^1/_{1000}$ kilometer
10 meters= **1 dekameter** =	$^1/_{10}$ hectometer	= $^1/_{100}$ kilometer
100 meters= 10 dekameters =	**1 hectometer**	= $^1/_{10}$ kilometer
1000 meters= 100 dekameters =	10 hectometers =	**1 kilometer**

Problem 2.26   1 kilometer (km) = _____dekameters

Solution 2.26   **100 dekameters** (see bottom line of Table 2)

Problem 2.27   100 millimeters = _____ centimeters

Solution 2.27   **10 centimeters** (see third line of equalities in Table 2)

By use of Table 2, unit changes of any dimension can be made quite easily. For example, to find out how many meters are in 25 dekameters, we can see that 10 meters are in one dekameter; so in 25 dekameters there are 10 times 25 meters or 250 meters.

Problem 2.28   How many hectometers are equivalent to 16 kilometers?

Solution 2.28   **160 hectometers** Since 1 km = 10 hectometers, then there are 16 × 10 hectometers in 16 km.

Table 3 shows the same conversion factors. To use Table 3, the units that are known are given on the top line and the units in the left column are the resulting conversions when the known quantities are multiplied by the constant.

To convert 40 centimeters to decimeters, locate centimeters (cm) in the top line, move down that column until the decimeter line (row) is encountered, and use the conversion factor which is .1. Simply multiply 40 cm by .1 and the answer is 4.0 decimeters. Let's try another. The conversion factor for changing hectometers (hm) to kilometers is .1. Then 75 hm = .1 × 75 or 7.5 km.

Problem 2.29   What is the conversion factor for changing dekameters to kilometers?

Solution 2.29   **.01** see Table 3. Thus to convert dekameters to kilometers, multiply by .01.

TABLE 3 WITHIN METRIC SYSTEM CONVERSION FACTORS

When you know*

Multiply To find:	mm	cm	dm	m	dk	hm	km
millimeter	1	10	100	1000	10000	100000	1000000
centimeter	.1	1	10	100	1000	10000	100000
decimeter	.01	.1	1	10	100	1000	10000
meter=	.001	.01	.1	1	10	100	1000
dekameter	.0001	.001	.01	.1	1	10	100
hectometer	.00001	.0001	.001	.01	.1	1	10
kilometer	.000001	.00001	.0001	.0001	.01	.1	1

*mm = millimeter   ' m = meter

cm = centimeter   dk = dekameter

dm = decimeter   hm = hectometer

km = kilometer

Problem 2.30   800 millimeters = _____ meters

Solution 2.30   **.8 or 8/10** 800 millimeters times the conversion
factor .001 is: 800 × .001 = .800. Note that the
zeros may be dropped and that .8 = .800.

Assume that we want to add four distances together which have
been measured in millimeters. Notice how easily the metric measures
may be expressed in several different units.

$$
\begin{array}{rl}
775 & \text{mm} \\
254 & \text{mm} \\
356 & \text{mm} \\
+\ 1104 & \text{mm} \\
\hline
2489 & \text{mm} \\
=\ 248.9 & \text{cm} \\
=\ 24.89 & \text{dm} \\
=\ 2.489 & \text{m}
\end{array}
$$

From this example you can see a pattern. If you are multiplying by 10, 100, or 1000, simply move the decimal to the right one, two, or three places respectively—the results are the same as if you multiplied it out the long way. Similarly, to multiply by .1, .01, .001; move the decimal to the left one, two, and three places respectively. For example, $249.32 \times 10 = 2493.2$. The decimal was moved one place to the right. Similarly, $249.32 \times 1000 = 249320$. A zero was added as a placeholder, but the principle was the same; the decimal was moved to the right three places. A little practice with this pattern will enable you to make within metric system conversions without pencil and paper—something that cannot generally be done with the English system of measurements.

Problem 2.31   Change 5296 millimeters to
a) centimeters
b) decimeters
c) meters
d) dekameters
e) hectometers

Solution 2.31 (Use Table 3)
a) **529.6** $5296 \times .1 = 529.6$
b) **52.96** $5296 \times .01 = 52.96$
c) **5.296** $5296 \times .001 = 5.296$
d) **.5296** $5296 \times .0001 = .5296$
e) **.05296** $5296 \times .00001 = .05296^*$

*in (e), a left zero was required as a placeholder.

It is necessary that the prefixes and their meaning be learned. Once you have a grasp of the prefixes, the conversions within the metric system can be mastered with a little practice. Consequently, it would be well to begin by memorizing the prefixes and their meanings given in Table 1. This will be an aid throughout the rest of the book as well. Exercises are provided at the end of the chapter for additional practice and familiarization purposes.

Chapter 2—Practice Exercises

I. Change the metric units to English units.

a) 20 cm = _____ inches   f) 14 m = _____ yds.
b) 20 m = _____ ft.   g) 100 m = _____ ft.
c) 88 mm = _____ inches   h) 86 cm = _____ inches
d) 100 cm = _____ inches   i) 450 km = _____ miles
e) 100 km = _____ miles   j) 95 m = _____ yds.

II. Change the English units to metric units.

a) 25 inches = _____ cm   f) .4 mile = _____ km
b) 220 yards = _____ meters g) 25 yards = _____ m
c) 480 miles = _____ km   h) 53 feet = _____ m
d) 5.9 ft. = _____ cm   i) 2.3 miles = _____ km
e) 9.3 ft. = _____ m   j) 4 inches = _____ mm

III. Convert within the metric system as indicated.

a) 400 m = _____ km
b) 20 cm = _____ mm
c) 5000 m = _____ km
d) 14 hectometers = _____ dekameters
e) 8 km = _____ m
f) 21 m = _____ cm
g) 1000 mm = _____ m
h) 1 decimeter = _____ dekameter
i) 400 mm = _____ cm
j) 9.6 m = _____ cm

Solutions to Chapter 2—Practice Exercises

I.
  a) 7.8 inches
  b) 65.62 feet
  c) 3.43 inches
  d) 39 inches
  e) 62.10 miles

  f) 15.31 yds.
  g) 328.08 ft.
  h) 33.54 inches
  i) 279.45 miles
  j) 103.89 yds.

II.
  a) 63.50 cm
  b) 201.17 meters
  c) 772.5 km
  d) 179.83 cm
  e) 2.83 m

  f) .64 km
  g) 22.86 m
  h) 16.15 m
  i) 3.7 km
  j) 101.60 mm

III.
  a) .4 km
  b) 200 mm
  c) 5 km
  d) 140 dekameters
  e) 8000 m

  f) 2100 cm
  g) 1 m
  h) .01 dekameters
  i) 40 cm
  j) 960 cm

3 MEASUREMENT OF AREA

Square units are generally used to describe area or the size of a two-dimensional object. Material may be measured in square feet, carpet in square yards, and land in sections (square miles). With the metric system of measurements, the square centimeter (cm²) is used for describing small areas. In building and construction the square meter (m²) is generally used. A square meter is approximately 20 percent larger than our familiar square yard. For larger areas, such as land measurement, the hectare (ha) is commonly used and is 10,000 square meters or approximately 2.5 acres.

Metric to English Conversion

As in Chapter II with the discussion of linear measurement, conversion from metric to English measurement of area will be shown using multiplication by a conversion factor (formula) and by graphical means; both of which are approximations. The formulas are more accurate than the interpretation of graphs and are suited for our common everyday use.

Smaller areas are treated first followed by common conversions for larger areas. The first conversion formula is for changing square centimeters to square inches. Since a centimeter is a unit of length, a square centimeter implies an area equal to a square that is one centimeter long and one centimeter wide. From Chapter 2, remember that a centimeter is about .4 of an inch in length. Formula 3.1 shows the conversion method if you are changing square centimeters to square inches.

(3.1)   Square Centimeters $\times$ 0.16 = Square Inches

Formula 3.1 says that a number of square centimeters multiplied by the constant conversion factor .16 will result in a number of square inches. For instance, to change 50 square centimeters to square inches, the following procedure would be used: 50 cm² × .16 = 8.00 in².

Problem 3.1   Change 15 square centimeters to sq. inches.

Solution 3.1   **2.4 sq. in.**

$$\begin{array}{r} 15 \text{ sq. cm.} \\ \times .16 \\ \hline 90 \\ 15 \\ \hline 2.40 \text{ sq. in.} \end{array}$$

Problem 3.2   How many square inches of wax paper would be required to cover the bottom of a pan with an area of 550 square centimeters?

Solution 3.2   **88 sq. in.**   550 cm² × .16 = 88.00 in²

Formula 3.2 can be used for converting square meters (m²) to square feet (ft²).

(3.2)   Square Meters × 10.76 = Square Feet

Again, Formula 3.2 is used in the same way as the formulas in Chapter 2 and the Formula 3.1 above. If you know a quantity of square meters and want to know the equivalent area in terms of square feet, Formula 3.2 indicates that you simply multiply the number of m² by 10.76 to obtain the answer.

Problem 3.3   65 square meters = _____ square feet

Solution 3.3   **699.4 sq. ft.**

$$\begin{array}{r} 10.76 \\ \times \ \ \ 65 \ \text{m}^2 \\ \hline 5380 \\ 6456 \ \ \\ \hline 699.40 \end{array}$$

(Remember to mark off 2 decimal places in the product)

Perhaps the conversion of square meters to square yards is of more practical use. Since a yard is just less than a meter, the two are used for measuring intermediate distances. Consequently, for expressing area, the square meter and the square yard may both be used for expressing similar sized regions. Formula 3.3 is used for this conversion.

(3.3)   Square meter $\times$ 1.2 = Square Yards

Problem 3.4   Convert 60 square meters to square yards.

Solution 3.4   **72 sq. yds.**   60 sq. m $\times$ 1.2 = 72 yd^2

Problem 3.5   If 35 square meters of carpet are required to cover a floor, how many sq. yards are required?

Solution 3.5   **42 sq. yds.**   35 $\times$ 1.2 = 42.0

For smaller land areas, the metric measurement used is the hectare (ha) which is 10,000 square meters. For similar plots, we are more accustomed to acres which is not a metric unit. Formula 3.4 shows the conversion factor for changing hectares to acres.

(3.4)   Hectares $\times$ 2.5 = Acres

Problem 3.6   A block of land set aside for a shopping center was 8 hectares. How many acres of land would this be?

Solution 3.6   **20 acres** $8 \times 2.5 = 20.0$

Problem 3.7   If a lot in a city is recorded as .4 hectare on the plat of survey, how large is the lot in terms of acres?

Solution 3.7   **1 acre** $.4 \times 2.5 = 1.00$

For expressing areas larger than can be conveniently described in acres, we usually use sections. A section of land is one square mile. In the metric system, the square kilometer can be used for expressing these larger areas. Formula 3.5 can be utilized for changing square kilometers (km^2) to square miles.

(3.5)   Square Kilometers $\times$ .4 = Square Miles

Problem 3.8   Change 10 km^2 to sections (sq. miles).

Solution 3.8   **4 sq. mi.** $10 \times .4 = 4.0$

Additional exercises are provided at the end of the chapter.

English to Metric Conversion

In this section we will be dealing with the same measures except the conversion problem will be one of changing English measures of area to metric measures. As with all of the previous conversions, the arithmetic process of multiplication will be used in conjunction with a conversion factor. In other words, each formula is set up so that a given or known quantity of English area units can be converted to metric equivalents by simply multiplying by the constant in the formula.

Formula 3.6 is the formula for converting square inches to square centimeters.

(3.6)   Square Inches $\times$ 6.5 = Square Centimeters

Roughly speaking then, each square inch of area contains 6.5 square centimeters of area. So, for "x" number of square inches, it logically follows that the number of square centimeters in "x" square inches would be "x" times 6.5.

Problem 3.9   Change 38 sq. inches to sq. cm.

Solution 3.9   **247 sq. cm.** $38 \times 6.5 = 247.0$

To change square feet and square yards to square meters, use Formula 3.7 and Formula 3.8 respectively. The conversion factor for changing square feet to square meters is .09 and for changing square yards to square meters, the multiplication constant is .84.

(3.7)   Square Feet $\times$ .09 = Square Meters
(3.8)   Square Yards $\times$ .84 = Square Meters

Problem 3.10   Change 40 square feet to square meters using Formula 3.7.

Solution 3.10   **3.6 m^2** $40 \times .09 = 3.60$

Problem 3.11   What is the conversion factor multiplier for changing yds^2 to sq. m.?

Solution 3.11   **.84**   (see Formula 3.8)

Problem 3.12   Use the Formula 3.8 and convert the area of a 24 square yard carpet to square meters.

Solution 3.12   **20.16 sq. m.** $24 \times .84 = 20.16$

To transform acre units to hectares, use Formula 3.9.

    (3.9)   **Acres $\times$ .4 = Hectares**

Problem 3.13   If you have a 2 acre plot of land, you may be asked to change this to the metric hectare unit for official records. What would your answer be?

Solution 3.13   **.8 hectares** $2 \times .4 = .8$

Problem 3.14   Which would be the larger, 60 acres of land or 50 hectares of land?

Solution 3.14   **50 ha** because 60 acres is equal to only $60 \times .4$ or 24 hectares.

Formula 3.10 shows the conversion from square miles to square kilometers.

    (3.10)   **Square Miles $\times$ 2.6 = Square Kilometers**

Problem 3.15   200 square miles = _____ square kilometers

Solution 3.15   **520 sq. km.** $200 \times 2.6 = 520.0$

Graphic Representation

The five graphs discussed in this section deal with the same conversions discussed in the two previous sections. As pointed out earlier, the graphic interpretation can be rapidly and efficiently utilized for rough and approximate conversions. If you have forgotten how to interpret line graphs, go to Chapter 1 and study the example shown. The technique of interpreting the graphical results is the same for all of the graphs in this manual. In all cases, the vertical axis is reserved for the metric system and the horizontal axis represents our English equivalents.

Figure 6 may be used to convert square inches to square centimeters or vice versa.

Notice that two small units on the horizontal axis represents one square inch. On the vertical axis, two of the smaller units represent five square centimeters. For review purposes, let's convert 20 square inches to square centimeters using Figure 6. First, locate 20 on the square inches or horizontal axis at the bottom of the graph. With a straightedge or a steady finger, move up to the line graph. Finally, with the straightedge or the same steady eye, move horizontally to the square centimeters or vertical axis. The approximate solution is 130 sq. cm.

Problem 3.16   Using Figure 6, estimate the conversion of 5 square inches to square centimeters.

Solution 3.16   **approx. 33 sq. cm.**

Problem 3.17   By reversing the process, estimate 150 sq. cm. in terms of sq. inches.

Solution 3.17   **approx. 23 sq. in.**

By using Figure 7, square feet-square meter conversions may be made. On the horizontal axis, each small unit represents 2 square feet

Square
Centimeters

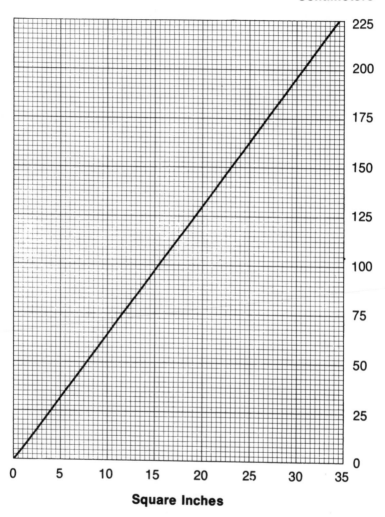

Square Inches

Figure 6 **Sq. Inch - Sq. Cm. Conversion**

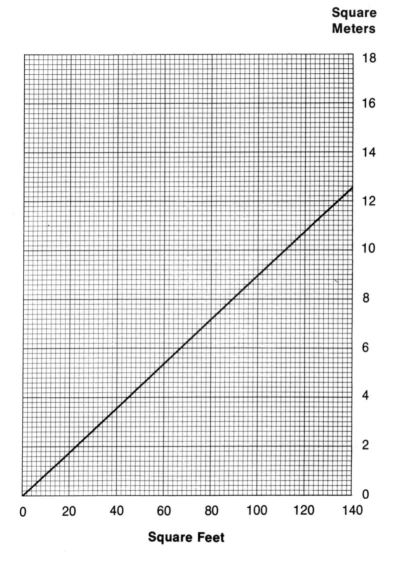

Square Meters

Square Feet

Figure 7 **Sq. Ft. - Sq. Meter Conversion**

41

and on the vertical axis, each small unit on the axis represents .2 of a square meter.

Problem 3.18   Estimate the number of square meters in 68 square feet using the graph in Figure 7.

Solution 3.18   **approx. 6 sq. m.**

Problem 3.19   Estimate the number of square feet in 10.8 square meters.

Solution 3.19   **approx. 120 sq. ft.**

The purpose of Figure 8 is to estimate conversions from square yards to square meters or square meters to square yards. Square yards are represented on the horizontal axis and each small unit on this axis is one square yard. The square meters axis is the vertical axis. On the vertical axis, one small unit on the graph is representative of one square meter.

Problem 3.20   20 sq. m. = _____ sq. yds.

Solution 3.20   **approx. 24 sq. yds.**

Problem 3.21   63 sq. yds. = _____ m²

Solution 3.21   **approx. 53 sq. m.**

Figures 9 and 10 are for conversion of larger areas. The horizontal axis units in Figure 9 are one acre and the vertical units for the same graph represent one-half hectare.

Problem 3.22   45 acres = _____hectares

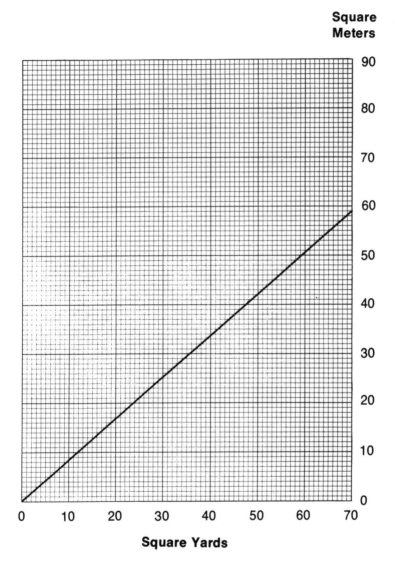

Figure 8 **Sq. Yard - Sq. Meter Conversion**

43

Hectares

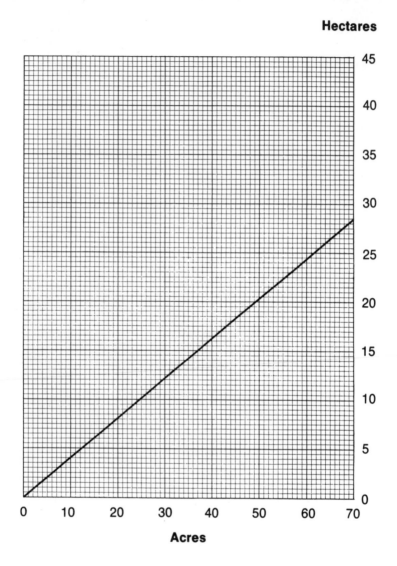

Acres

Figure 9 **Acre - Hectare Conversion**

44

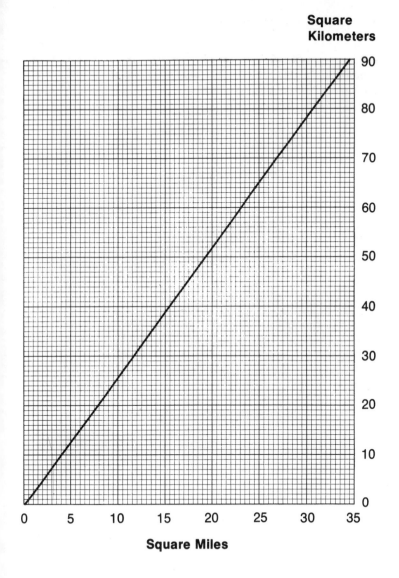

Square Kilometers

Square Miles

Figure 10 **Sq. Mile - Sq. Kilometer Conversion**

45

Solution 3.22   **approx. 18½ ha.**

The small units on the horizontal axis of Figure 10 represent one-half square mile. The vertical axis is the square kilometer axis and each unit is one square kilometer.

Problem 3.23   Convert via Figure 10 twenty square miles to square km.

Solution 3.23   **approx. 51.5 sq. km.**

Problem 3.24   78 sq. km. = _____ sq. mi.

Solution 3.24   **approx. 30 sq. mi.**

Metric to Metric Conversion

The common metric area measures are given in Table 4. Notice that since area is typically measured in *square* units, the subdivisions and multiples of adjacent measurements are multiples of 10 squared or 100 rather than 10 as with linear measures. This relationship is seen in Table 4.

TABLE 4 **METRIC SYSTEM AREA**

Unit	Symbol	Relationship
Square centimeter	cm^2	$1\ cm^2 = 100\ mm^2$
Square decimeter	dm^2	$1\ dm^2 = 100\ cm^2$
Square meter	m^2	$1\ m^2 = 100\ dm^2$
Are (sq. dekameter)	a	$1\ a = 100\ m^2$
Hectare	ha	$1\ ha = 100\ a$
Square kilometer	km^2	$1\ km^2 = 100\ ha$

For computational conversion, Table 5 shows the multiplier constant. To use Table 5 for within metric conversion, the top row of symbols times the conversion factor below it will yield units corresponding to the symbols in the left column.

TABLE 5 **AREA CONVERSION WITHIN THE METRIC SYSTEM**

When you know

Multiply to find:	cm²	dm²	m²	a	ha	km²
cm²	1	100	10000	10^6	10^8	10^{10}
dm²	.01	1	100	10000	10^6	10^8
m²	.0001	.01	1	100	10000	10^6
a	10^{-6}	.0001	.01	1	100	10000
ha	10^{-8}	10^{-6}	.0001	.01	1	100
km²	10^{-10}	10^{-8}	10^{-6}	.0001	.01	1

Extremely large conversion factors are expressed as powers of tens. For instance, to convert square kilometers to square centimeters, the conversion factor is 10^{10} which is 10000000000. It's not very frequently that we need or even want to make these kinds of conversions. Also, to convert cm² to km², the same type computational problem is encountered. That is 10^{-10} is .0000000001 and this type transformation is very seldom required—its kind of like converting square inches to square miles—sort of ridiculous. An example will help clarify the use of the table. Suppose that we want to convert 500 square decimeters (dm²) to square meters (m²). First, locate dm² on the top line and move down that column until the conversion factor is found corresponding to m² which is the third number down. The factor is .01. Then the solution is 500 × .01 or 5 sq. meters.

Problem 3.25   Change 20 m² (sq. meters) to:
        a) dm² (square decimeters)
        b) a (ares)
        c) ha (hectares)

Solution 3.25   a) **2000 dm²**   20 × 100 = 2000
        b) **.2 a**   20 × .01 = .20
        c) **.002 ha**   20 × .0001 = .0020

Chapter 3—Practice Exercises

I. Change metric area units to English units of area.

a) 22 sq. cm. = _____ sq. in.   f) 14 sq. m. = _____ sq. ft.
b) 25 sq. m. = _____ sq. ft.   g) 45 sq. m. = _____ sq. yds.
c) 90 sq. km. = _____ sq. mi.   h) 6.8 km² = _____ sq. miles
d) 32 sq. m. = _____ sq. yd.   i) 48 sq. cm. = _____ sq. inch
e) 500 hectares = _____ acres   j) 4.3 ha = _____ acres

II. Change English area to metric units of area.

a) 25 sq. yds. = _____m²   f) 3.5 acres = _____ ha
b) 30 acres = _____ ha   g) 100 sq. ft. = _____ sq. meters
c) 9 sq. in. = _____ sq. cm.   h) 500 sq. mi. = _____ sq. km.
d) 31 sq. miles = _____ km²   i) 50 sq. in. = _____ sq. cm.
e) 5.5 sq. in. = _____ cm²   j) 1.8 sq. miles = _____ km²

III. Convert within the metric system as indicated.

a) 50 m² = _____ ares   f) 5000 cm² = _____ m²
b) 600 a = _____ ha   g) 33 a = _____ m²
c) 950 dm² _____ a   h) 10,000 m² = _____ a
d) 3 dm² = _____ cm²   i) 4 km² = _____ a
e) 100 ha = _____ km²   j) 6 km² = _____ m²

Solutions to Chapter 3—Practice Exercises

I.   a) 3.52 sq. in.
      b) 270 sq. ft.
      c) 36 sq. mi.
      d) 38.4 sq. yd.
      e) 1250 acres

    f) 151.2 sq. ft.
    g) 54 sq. yds.
    h) 2.72 sq. miles
    i) 7.68 sq. inches
    j) 10.75 acres

II.   a) 21 m^2
      b) 12 ha
      c) 58.50 sq. cm.
      d) 80.6 km^2
      e) 35.75 cm^2

    f) 1.4 ha
    g) 9 sq. meters
    h) 1300 sq. km.
    i) 325 sq. cm.
    j) 4.68 km^2

III. a) .5 ares
      b) 6 ha
      c) .095 a
      d) 300 cm^2
      e) 1 km^2

    f) .5 m^2
    g) 3300 m^2
    h) 100 a
    i) 40000 a
    j) 6×10^6 m^2 or 6,000,000 m^2

4 MEASUREMENTS OF VOLUME, CAPACITY AND LIQUIDS

In this chapter, the discussion will center on volume and capacity. Typically, we can use the same measurement terminology to describe both. Volume can be thought of as the amount of space occupied by an object whereas capacity refers to how much a container will hold. Volume and capacity may be expressed as cubic units and are three-dimensional concepts. A cubic unit may be thought of as the size of a block (cube) one unit high, one unit wide, and one unit long. Thus a cubic inch block occupies space one inch long, one inch wide, and one inch high.

Although capacity may be expressed in cubic units, other convenient units for liquid and dry measure have traditionally been used such as quarts, bushels, teaspoons, ounces, etc. The metric system for volume and capacity is similar; however, cubic units in the metric system are directly related to liquid measure units. Further, liquid and dry measures are measured with the same units which eliminates ambiguities that have existed in our present system.

Table 6 is a review of the formulas for finding the volume of several common solids that are frequently encountered.

TABLE 6 **VOLUME FORMULAS FOR COMMON SOLIDS**

Solid	Formula

Cube

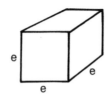

$V = e^3 = e \times e \times e$

Rectangular Prism

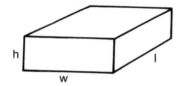

$V = l \times w \times h$

Triangular Prism

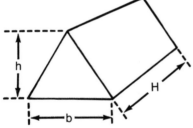

$V = \frac{1}{2} \times b \times h \times H$

Rectangular Pyramid

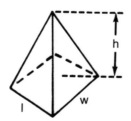

$V = \frac{1}{3} \times l \times w \times h$

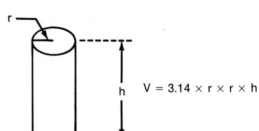

Cylinder

$$V = 3.14 \times r \times r \times h$$

Cone

$$V = \tfrac{1}{3} \times 3.14 \times r^2 \times h$$

Sphere (Ball)

$$V = \tfrac{4}{3} \times 3.14 \times r^3$$

Problem 4.1   Find the volume of a cube that is 2 inches on an edge, i.e., e = 2 inches.

Solution 4.1   **8 cubic inches**   V = 2 × 2 × 2 = 8 cu in

Problem 4.2   A rectangular prism is 1 ft. long, 2 ft. wide, and 3 ft. high. What is the volume?

Solution 4.2   **6 cu. ft.** $V = 1 \times 2 \times 3 = 6$

Problem 4.3   Assume that you are the first person from earth to arrive at a planet in a distant solar system.
Further assume that the inhabitants of the planet and you work out a unit of length called a xlifrz. They present you with a cylinder which is 3 xlifrzs high (h) and the base has a radius (r) of 10 xlifrzs. They want you to figure the volume.

Solution 4.3   **942 cubic xlifrzs** $V = 3.14 \times 10 \times 10 \times 3 = 942.00$

Problem 4.4   A cone is 3 inches high (h) and the base has a radius of 10 inches. What is the volume?

Solution 4.4   **314 cu. in.** $V = \frac{1}{3} \times 3.14 \times 100 \times 3 = 314.00$

Metric to English Conversion

Common sizes that we have used include cubic inches, cubic feet, and cubic yards for expressing volume. In the metric system, cubic centimeters and cubic meters are frequently used. Therefore formulas 4.1, 4.2, and 4.3 are useful for converting metric cubic units to English cubic units.

Formula 4.1 is the conversion formula for changing cubic centimeters to cubic inches. The constant which is multiplied by the known number of cubic centimeters resulting in a number of cubic inches is 0.06.

(4.1)   Cubic Centimeters × .06 = Cubic Inches

Problem 4.5　　Change 50 cubic centimeters to cubic inches.

Solution 4.5　　**3 cubic inches**　$50 \text{ cm}^3 \times .06 = 3.00 \text{ in}^3$

Problem 4.6　　A rectangular prism is 3 cm. wide, 10 cm. long, and 5 cm. high. Find the volume of the prism in cubic cm. and convert to cubic inches.

Solution 4.6　　**9 cu. in.**　　$V = 10 \text{cm} \times 3 \text{ cm} \times 5 \text{ cm} = 150 \text{ cm}^3$
$150 \text{ cm}^3 \times .06 = 9.00 \text{ cu. in.}$

Another common conversion is from cubic meters (m^3) to cubic feet (ft^3) and cubic yards (yd^3). Formula 4.2 and Formula 4.3 may be used to change m^3 to cubic feet and cubic yards respectively.

(4.2)　**Cubic Meters $\times$ 35 = Cubic Feet**
(4.3)　**Cubic Meters $\times$ 1.3 = Cubic Yards**

Problem 4.7　　8 cubic meters = _____ cubic feet

Solution 4.7　　**280 cu. ft.**　　$8 \times 35 = 280$

Problem 4.8　　What capacity (in cubic yards) truck would be required to carry 5 cubic meters of sand?

Solution 4.8　　**6.5 cu. yds.**　　$5m^3 \times 1.3 = 6.5 \text{ yds}^3$

Another basic unit of capacity in the metric system is the liter (l). For comparison purposes, the liter is just a little larger than the U.S. liquid quart, but smaller than the U.S. dry quart and the British Imperial quart. The liter can be used for measuring both liquid and dry contents. One-thousandths of a liter is called a milliliter (ml) which is commonly used in scientific and pharmaceutical work—it is the same as one cubic centimeter (1 cc).

Formulas 4.4 through 4.8 are for conversion from the metric system of capacity to U.S. units.

(4.4) **Milliliters (cc's) $\times$ .03 = Fluid ounces**
(4.5) **Liters $\times$ 2.1 = Pints**
(4.6) **Liters $\times$ 1.06 = Liquid Quarts**
(4.7) **Liters $\times$ .91 = Dry Quarts**
(4.8) **Liters $\times$ .26 = Gallons**

Problem 4.9   Change 300 milliliters (cu. cc's) to fluid ounces.

Solution 4.9   **9 fl. oz.**   300 ml $\times$ .03 = 9.00 fl. oz.

Problem 4.10   10 liters = _____ pints

Solution 4.10   **21 pints**   10 l $\times$ 2.1 = 21 pints

Problem 4.11   Change 6 liters to: a) liquid quarts, b) dry quarts, and c) gallons.

Solution 4.11   a) **6.36 liquid**   6 l $\times$ 1.06 = 6.36 liquid qts.
                qts.
                b) **5.46 dry qts.** 6 l $\times$ .91 = 5.46 dry qts.
                c) **1.56 gallons** 6 l $\times$ .26 = 1.56 gal.

English to Metric Conversion

In this section, conversions not only for the construction worker and handiman, but also the household cook are given. First, let's consider the conversion of some liquid measures from the English system to the metric scheme. Formulas 4.9 through 4.15 may be used for this purpose. Keep in mind that the conversions are approximations, but that they are sufficient for most of our practical day to day use. The simplicity of working with only a minimum number of decimal places coupled with ever present measurement errors form the rationale for using approximations that are appropriate for common usage.

(4.9)	**Teaspoons × 5 = Milliliters**
(4.10)	**Tablespoons × 15 = Milliliters**
(4.11)	**Fluid Ounces × 30 = Milliliters**
(4.12)	**Cups × .24 = Liters**
(4.13)	**Pints × .47 = Liters**
(4.14)	**Liquid Quarts × .95 = Liters**
(4.15)	**Gallons × 3.8 = Liters**

Problem 4.12   Change units as indicated.
a) 6 teaspoons = _____ ml.
b) 2 tablespoons = _____ ml.
c) 2.5 fl. oz. = _____ ml.

Solution 4.12
a) **30 ml**   6 teaspoons × 5 = 30 milliliters
b) **30 ml**   2 tablespoons × 15 = 30 milliliters
c) **75 ml**   2.5 fl. oz. × 30 = 75 ml.

Problem 4.13   Change the following quantities to liters.
a) 3.5 cups
b) 5 pints
c) .5 gallon
d) 4 liquid quarts

Solution 4.13
a) **.84 liter**   3.5 cups × .24 = .840 l
b) **2.35 liters**   5 pts. × .47 = 2.35 l
c) **1.9 liter**   .5 gal. × 3.8 = 1.90 l
d) **3.8 liter**   4 qts. × .95 = 3.80 liters by Formula 4.14 or
4 qts. = 1 gal. = 3.8 by Formula 4.15

To make changes from English cubic units of volume to metric cubic units, Formulas 4.16, 4.17, and 4.18 may be utilized.

(4.16)	**Cubic Inches × 16.38 = Cubic Centimeters**
(4.17)	**Cubic Feet × .03 = Cubic Meters**
(4.18)	**Cubic Yards × .76 = Cubic Meters**

Problem 4.14 Change 5 cubic inches to cubic centimeters.

Solution 4.14 **81.9 cu. cm.** 5 in³ × 16.38 = 81.90 cm³

Problem 4.15 Convert the following volumes to cubic meters (m³).
a) 100 cu. ft. b) 12 cu. yds.

Solution 4.15 a) **3 cu. m.** 100 ft³ × .03 = 3.00 cu. m.
b) **9.12 cu. m.** 12 yds³ × .76 = 0.12 cu. m.

Graphic Conversions

Figures 11-20 are graphical representations of the same conversions discussed in the preceding two sections. The graphs are presented to enable quick, but rough, estimates for conversions from one system to another. You may want to review the illustration in Chapter 1 before examining the graphs that follow.

Below are ten problems, one from each graph representation, for you to check your interpretation skills.

Problem 4.16 Use Figures 11 through 20 to estimate the conversions as indicated.

a) 10 cu. in. =_____ cu. cm.   f) 80 ml = _____ tablespoons

b) 12 cu. m. = _____ cu. ft.   g) 8.2 cups = _____ liters

c) 46 cu. yds. = _____ cu. m.   h) 10 pints = _____ liters

d) 120 ml. = _____ fl. oz.   i) 10 liters = _____ quarts

e) 4 teaspoons = _____ ml.   j) 8 gal. = _____ l.

Solution 4.16

a) **160 cu. cm.** (Fig. 11)   f) **5.35 tablespoons** (fig. 16)

b) **400 cu. ft.** (Fig. 12)   g) **2 liters** (fig. 17)

c) **35 cu. yds.** (Fig. 13)   h) **4.7 liters** (Fig. 18)

d) **4 Fl. oz.** (Fig. 14)   i) **10.4 quarts** (Fig. 19)

e) **20 ml.** (Fig. 15)   j) **30.5 l.** (Fig. 20)

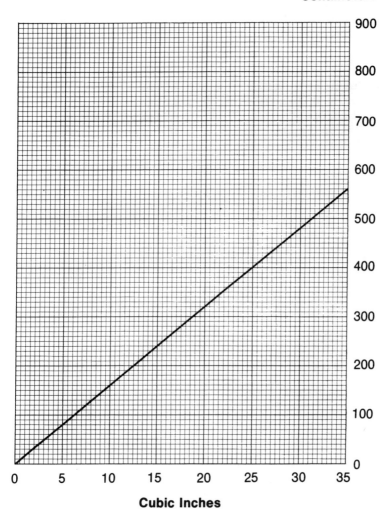

Cubic Centimeters

Cubic Inches

Figure 11 **Cu. Inch - Cu. Centimeter Conversion**

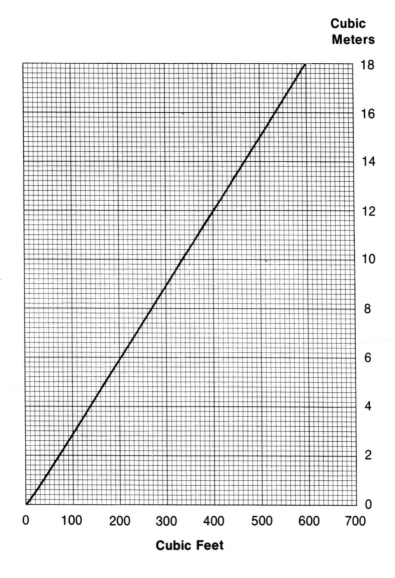

Cubic Meters

Cubic Feet

Figure 12 **Cubic Feet - Cubic Meter Conversion**

**Cubic
Meters**

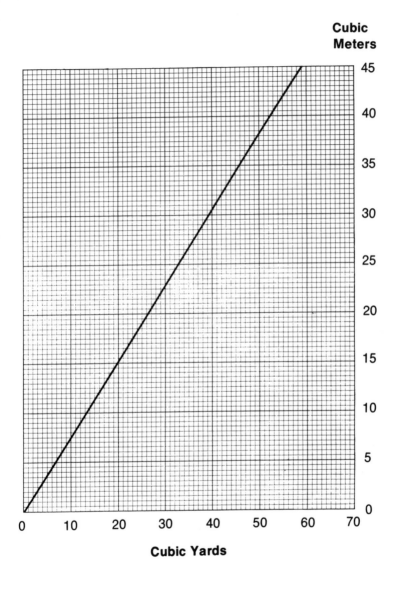

Cubic Yards

Figure 13 **Cubic Yard - Cubic Meter Conversion**

Milliliters

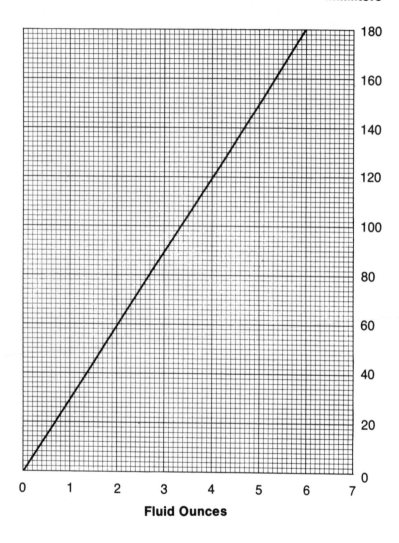

Fluid Ounces

Figure 14 **Fl. Ounce - Milliliter Conversion**

Milliliters

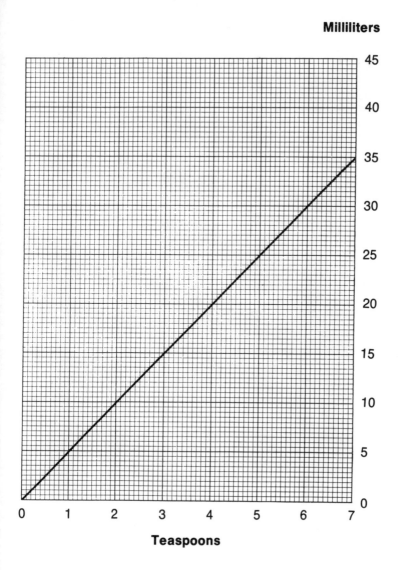

Teaspoons

Figure 15 **Teaspoon - Milliliter Conversion**

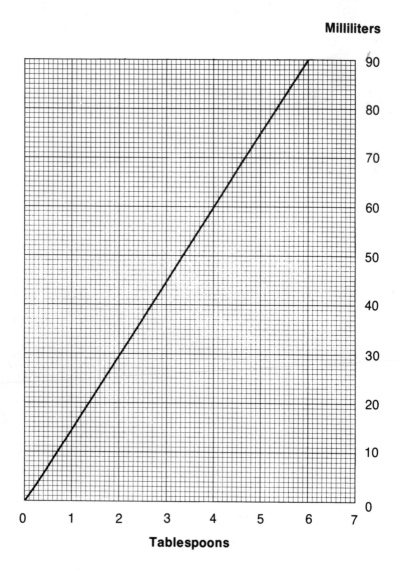

Milliliters

Tablespoons

Figure 16 **Tablespoon - Milliliter Conversion**

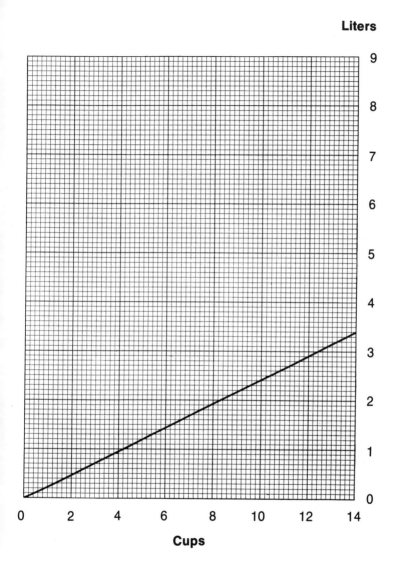

Figure 17 **Cup - Liter Conversion**

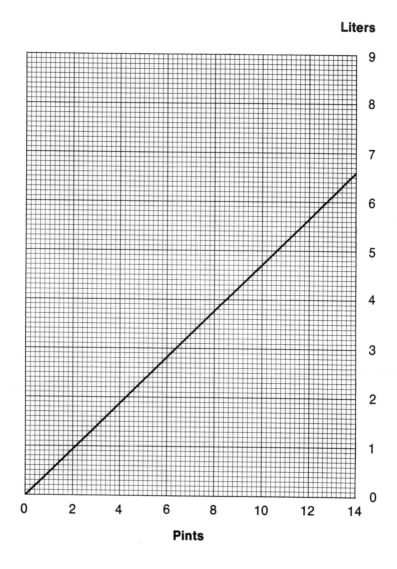

Figure 18 **Pint - Liter Conversion**

Liters

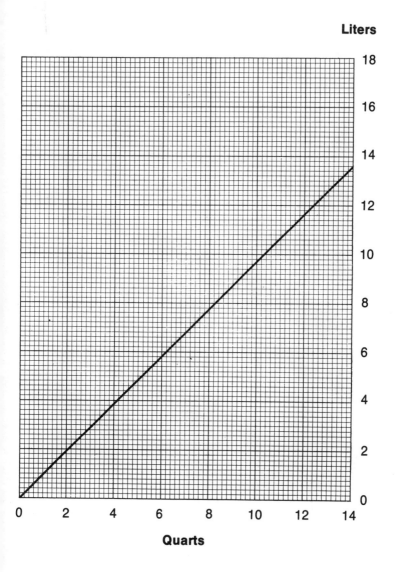

Quarts

Figure 19 **Quart - Liter Conversion**

Liters

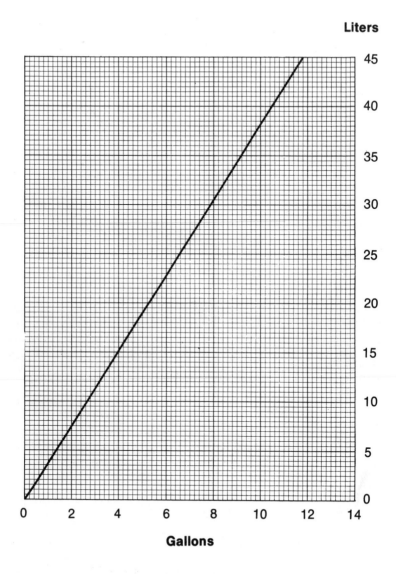

Gallons

Figure 20 **Gallon - Liter Conversion**

Metric to Metric Conversion

The cubic meter (m^3) is the basic unit for metric volume. However, since the cubic meter is too large for most household uses, subdivisions of the cubic meter have more utility for most of our needs. Probably the most convenient unit of volume in the metric system is the cubic decimeter (dm^3) which is 1,000 cubic millimeters or one liter. For scientific and drug dispensing, the millimeter (cubic centimeter) is widely used. For measurements of concrete, sand, and excavation, the cubic meter (m^3) is appropriate.

Conversion factors for converting within the metric system by multiplication are given in Table 7. Notice that a conversion factor of 1 would indicate that the volume is the same for the two quantities. For example, one cubic centimeter is equivalent to one milliliter. To make use of Table 7, the top row is assumed to be known. The conversion factor corresponding to the other units are directly below the known quantity.

TABLE 7 WITHIN METRIC SYSTEM CONVERSION

	*When you know**				
Multiply to find:	cm^3	ml	dm^3	l	m^3
cm^3	1	1	1000	1000	1,000,000
ml	1	1	1000	1000	1,000,000
dm^3	.001	.001	1	1	1,000
l	.001	.001	1	1	1,000
m^3	.000001	.000001	.001	.001	1

*cm^3 = cubic centimeters   l = liters
ml = milliliters m^3 = cubic meters
dm^3 = cubic decimeters

An example: to change 4 liters to milliliters, first locate l on the top row. Below "l", 1,000 is shown as the conversion factor on the "ml" line. Therefore, multiply 4 × 1000 which is 4000 ml.

Problem 4.17   Change 17 ml to cubic centimeters.

Solution 4.17   **17 cubic**   17 ml × 1 = 17 cc
                 centimeters   since 1 cm³ = 1 ml.

___

Problem 4.18   Convert 400 liters to cubic meters.

Solution 4.18   **.4 cu. m.**   400 l × .001 = .400 m³

___

Problem 4.19   Change 10,000 ml to liters.

Solution 4.19   **10 liters**   10,000 ml × .001 = 10.000 l

Chapter 4—Practice Exercises

I. Change the given quantity of liters to liquid quarts, dry quarts, and gallons as indicated.

	Liters	Liquid Quarts	Dry Quarts	Gallons
a)	10	_____	_____	_____
b)	22	_____	_____	_____
c)	50	_____	_____	_____
d)	160	_____	_____	_____
e)	5	_____	_____	_____

II. Change the following metric units of volume to the indicated English cubic units or liquid measure.

a) 400 cu. cm. = _____ cu. in
b) 2.1 cu. meters = _____ cu. ft.
c) 10 cu. meters = _____ cu. yds.
d) 30 milliliters = _____ fl. oz.
e) 1500 cm^3 = _____ in^3
f) 3 m^3 = _____ yds^3
g) 2.34 l = _____ pints.
h) 12 cu. meters = _____ yds^3
i) 536 cu. cm. = _____ cu. in.
j) 3 m^3 = _____ ft^3

III. Convert the following liquid measures to the metric unit equivalent.

a) 20 teaspoons = _____ ml
b) 5 cups = _____ liters
c) 1 quart = _____ liters
d) 1.5 tablespoons = _____ milliliters
e) 16 fl. oz. = _____ ml
f) 13 pints = _____ l
g) 2 gal = _____ liters
h) 2.5 teaspoons = _____ ml.
i) 3.4 gal = _____ liters
j) 4.6 qts. = _____ l

IV. Change as indicated

a) 4 liters + 2 liters = _____ milliliters
b) 600 ml = _____ liters
c) 7 m^3 = _____ dm^3
d) 6 dm^3 = _____ m^3
e) 2 m^3 = _____ cm^3

Solutions to Chapter 4—Practice Exercises

I.
	Liquid Quarts	Dry Quarts	Gallons
a)	10.57	9.08	2.64
b)	23.25	19.98	5.81
c)	52.84	45.40	13.21
d)	169.1	145.3	42.3
e)	5.28	4.54	1.32

II.
a) 24		f) 3.9
b) 23.5		g) 4.914
c) 13		h) 15.6
d) .9		i) 32.16
e) 90		j) 105

III.
a) 100		f) 6.11
b) 1.2		g) 7.6
c) .95		h) 12.5
d) 22.5		i) 12.92
e) 480		j) 4.37

IV.
a) 6000
b) .6
c) 7,000
d) .006
e) 2,000,000

5 WEIGHTS

In the previous chapters, measurements describing the concepts of size in terms of linear distance, area and volume were discussed. In this chapter and the next, concepts which are not necessarily concerned with the size of physical measurements are discussed. One of these concepts is weight or mass. As described in Chapter 1, weight may be considered a force—that force of gravity between an object and the earth. We describe weights in various units—ounces, drams, pounds, tons, and so forth. In the metric system, the gram (g) is the basic unit of weight. The gram is too small for convenience except for pharmaceutical and scientific work. Actually, it requires approximately 30 grams to equal one avoirdupois ounce. Consequently, the kilogram (1000 g) is a more appropriate unit for most of our purposes. A kilogram (kg) is about 2.2 pounds. For expressing large weights such as farm commodities, the metric ton (1000 kg) is convenient. Incidently, it might be of interest that one liter of water weighs one kilogram for all practical purposes.

Metric to English Conversion

In this section, the following conversions are presented: grams to ounces, kilograms to ounces and pounds, and metric tons (megagrams) to tons. In our customary system, the ounces will refer to avoirdupois ounces and the ton to the short ton (2,000 lbs.).

Formula 5.1 is for changing a known number of grams (g) to ounces.

(5.1)   Grams × 0.35 = Ounces

To change 520 grams to ounces, we multiply thusly;

520 g × .035 = 18.2 ounces.

Problem 5.1   *If you sweetened your ice tea with 25 grams of
             sugar, what portion of an ounce of sugar would
             this be?

Solution 5.1   **.875 ounce**   25 × .035 = .875

Problem 5.2   Change 700 grams to ounces

Solution 5.2   **24.5 ounces**   700 × .035 = 24.500

Formulas 5.2 and 5.3 show the conversion procedures for changing kilograms to ounces and pounds respectively by multiplication.

> **(5.2)   Kilograms × 35.27 = Ounces**
> **(5.3)   Kilograms × 2.2 = Pounds**

Problem 5.3   Convert 2.6 kilograms to a) ounces, and b)
             pounds.

Solution 5.3   a) **91.702**   2.6 × 35.27 = 91.702
             ounces
             b) **5.72 pounds**   2.6 × 2.2 = 5.72

In the metric system, a megagram is the designation for 1,000,000
grams. This quantity is also 1,000 kg and in most circles is referred to
as a metric ton when heavier weights are described. Formula 5.4
shows the relationship between the metric ton and the English short
ton (2,000 lbs.).

> **(5.4)   Metric Tons × 1.1 = Tons**

Problem 5.4   Change 4 metric tons to tons.

Solution 5.4	**4.4 tons**	$4 \times 1.1 = 4.4$

Problem 5.5	6.2 megagrams = _____ tons

Solution 5.5	**6.82 tons**	$6.2 \times 1.1 = 6.82$

English to Metric Conversion

Three formulas for converting to the metric units of weights are discussed in this section. Formula 5.5 may be used to change ounces to grams.

(5.5)   Ounces × 28 = Grams

Problem 5.6   Change 20 ounces to grams.

Solution 5.6   **560 grams** $20 \times 28 = 560$

Formula 5.6 is for converting pounds to kilograms. In weights, these units are the most widely used in our daily household affairs.

(5.6)   Pounds × .45 = Kilograms

Problem 5.7   If a man weighs 160 lbs., express his weight in kilograms.

Solution 5.7   **72 kg** $160 \times .45 = 72.00$

Tons are converted to metric tons by multiplying the number of tons by 0.9 as shown in Formula 5.7.

(5.7)   Tons × .9 = Metric Tons (Megagrams)

Problem 5.8	If a farmer sold 6 tons of grain for $60 per metric ton, how much money would be receive?

Solution 5.8	**$324.00**	6 tons × .9 = 5.4 metric tons
		5.4 × $60 = $324.00

Graphic Representation

As in previous chapters, the relationships discussed in this chapter can be expressed by means of a line graph. Figure 21 shows the linear relationship between ounces and grams. The small horizontal axis units each represent .1 of an ounce while the small units in the vertical axis represents 2 units (grams) each.

Problem 5.9	Using the graph in Figure 21, 3 ounces is approximately how many grams?

Solution 5.9	**84 grams**

Figure 22 may be used for pound-kilogram conversion. Each small unit on the horizontal (pound) axis is one pound. Each small vertical unit represents ½ kilogram.

Problem 5.10	Change 20 kg to lbs. using Figure 22.

Solution 5.10	**45 lbs.**

Finally, Figure 23 shows the relationship between the heavy weights—metric tons and tons. The small vertical and horizontal units on the graph represent one metric ton and one ton respectively.

Problem 5.11	45 metric tons = _____ tons.

Solution 5.11	**50 tons**

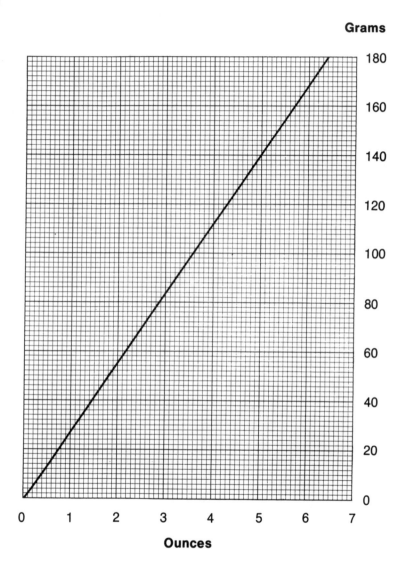

Grams

Figure 21 **Ounce - Gram Conversion**

Kilograms

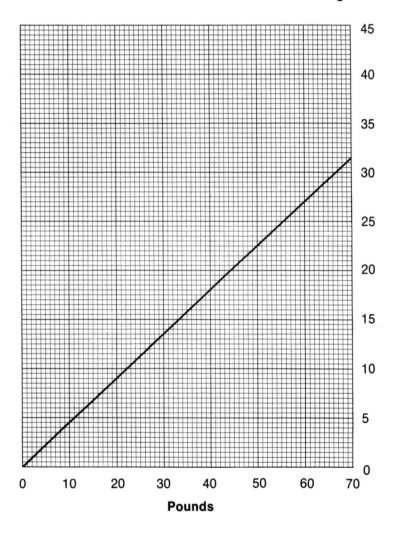

Pounds

Figure 22 **Pound - Kilogram Conversion**

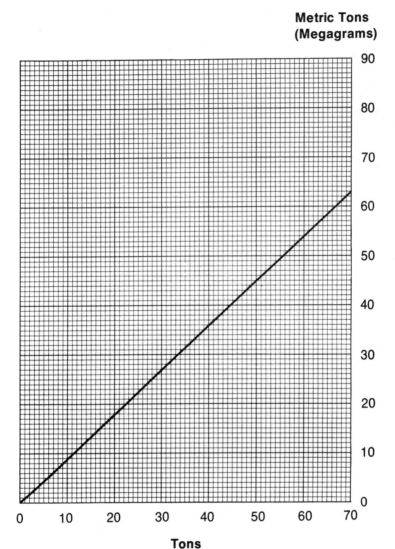

Metric Tons (Megagrams)

Tons

Figure 23 **Ton - Metric ton Conversion**

Metric to Metric Conversion

The same prefixes describe multiples (or subdivisions) of the basic unit of weight as were used in Chapter 2 to describe length or linear measures. However, the more common units of weight in the metric system are the milligram (one-thousandths of a gram), the gram, the kilogram (1,000 grams), and the metric ton (1,000 kg).

Table 8 shows the multiplication conversion factor for these metric weights. To use Table 8, multiply the quantities in the top row by the conversion factor directly below it corresponding to the units desired. That is, to change 900 grams (g) to kg., locate grams on the top row. The conversion factor below "g" which corresponds to kg is .001. Thus, .001 × 900 grams = .9 kg.

TABLE 8 **WITHIN METRIC SYSTEM WEIGHT CONVERSION**

Multiply to find:	When you know*			
	mg	g	kg	t
mg	1	1000	1000000	10^9
g	.001	1	1000	1000000
kg	.000001	.001	1	1000
t	10^{-9}	.000001	.001	1

*mg	= milligram	kg = kilogram
g	= gram	t = metric ton (megagrams)

Problem 5.12 1500 g = _____ kg.

Solution 5.12 **1.5 kg**   1500 × .001 = 1.500

Problem 5.13 _____ kg = 5 metric tons

Solution 5.13 **5,000 kg**   5 × 1,000 = 5,000

Problem 5.14 2 metric tons = _____ grams

Solution 5.14 **2 million g.** 2 × 1,000,000 = 2,000,000

Chapter 5—Practice Exercises

Convert the units of weight as indicated.

1) 113 metric tons = _____ tons
2) 400 kilograms = _____ pounds
3) 60 ounces = _____ grams = _____ kg.
4) 12 tons = _____ metric tons = _____ kg.
5) 12 kg. = _____ ounces
6) 16 grams = _____ ounces
7) 170 kg = _____ lbs.
8) 10.6 metric tons = _____ tons
9) 100 lbs. = _____ kilograms = _____ grams
10) 3 metric tons = _____ kg. = _____ grams

Solutions to Chapter 5—Practice Exercises

1) 124.3
2) 440
3) 1680, 1.68
4) 10.8, 10800
5) 423.24
6) 0.56
7) 374
8) 11.66
9) 45, 45000
10) 3000, 3,000,000

6 TEMPERATURE

Although the metric system does not provide us with a metric temperature scale, it is significant that all countries that use the metric system of weights and measures also use the Celsius scale for describing temperature. The Celsius scale is the same as the centigrade scale which has relatively widespread use even in non-metric countries. The Celsius (centigrade) scaling results in a reading of 0° at the freezing point of water and 100° at the boiling point of water.

Celsius to Fahrenheit Conversion

The freezing point on the Fahrenheit scale is 32° and the boiling point is 212°F., whereas on the Celsius scale the equivalent readings are zero and 100°C. Notice at freezing, the Fahrenheit scale starts off 32° "ahead" of the Celsius scale. Further note that the difference between the boiling point and the freezing point on the Fahrenheit and Celsius scales is 180 and 100 units respectively. Then the ratio of Fahrenheit to Celsius units is 180 to 100, or 9 to 5 in lowest terms. Consequently, to change Celsius units to Fahrenheit units, we must add 32° to 9/5 of the number of Celsius units. Formula 6.1 details this relationship.

$$(6.1) \quad F = (9/5 \times C) + 32 \text{ or}$$
$$F = (1.8 \times C) + 32$$

Problem 6.1   Change 30° to Fahrenheit degrees.

Solution 6.1	**86°F**	$F = (9/5 \times 30) + 32$
		$= 54 + 32$
		$= 86$

Problem 6.2   Change $-40°$ C to F.

Solution 6.2	**−40° F.**	$F = (9/5 \times -40) + 32$
		$= -72 + 32$
		$= -40$

Fahrenheit to Celsius Conversion

With a few algebraic manipulations of Formula 6.1, the value of C can be obtained. Formula 6.2 gives this solution and can be used to convert Fahrenheit degrees to Celsius degrees.

$$\textbf{(6.2)} \quad \textbf{C} = \textbf{5/9} \times \textbf{(F} - \textbf{32)}$$

In Formula 6.2, the first operation is shown inside of the parentheses. That is, the Fahrenheit reading is reduced by 32 *before* being multiplied by 5/9.

Problem 6.3   Normal body temperature is about 98° F. What would this reading be on a centigrade scale?

Solution 6.3	**35.6° C**	$C = 5/9 \times (98 - 32)$
		$= 5/9 \times (66)$
		$= 35.55. \ldots$

Graphic Representation

From Figure 24, an approximation of the conversion from one temperature scale to the other can be accomplished. On the horizontal axis, each small unit represents 5° F. The large units (10 small units) on the vertical axis each represent 25° C.

Problem 6.4   0° C. = _____° F. (Use Figure 24)

Solution 6.4   **32° F**

Problem 6.5   255° F = _____° C.

Solution 6.5   **125° C**

Chapter 6—Practice Exercises

I. Given below are Celsius temperature readings. Convert them to Fahrenheit equivalents.

a) 9   f) 117
b) 17   g) 119
c) 45   h) 149
d) 51   i) 11.5
e) 101   j) 129

II. Change the following Fahrenheit temperatures to Celsius (centigrade) degrees.

a) 77   f) 23
b) 85   g) 11
c) 127   h) 149
d) 139   i) 7
e) 99   j) 33

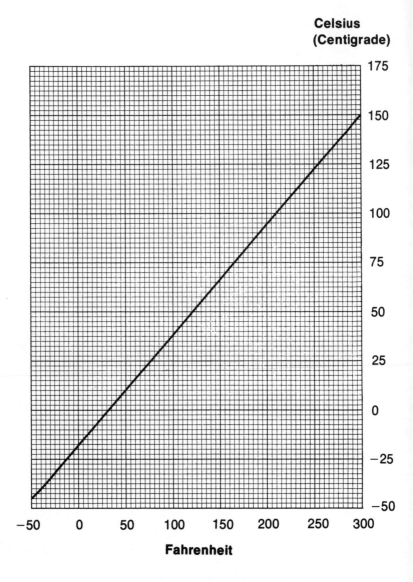

Figure 24 **Fahrenheit - Celsius Conversion**

Solutions to Chapter 6—Practice Exercises

I.
a) 48.20
b) 62.60
c) 113.00
d) 123.80
e) 213.80

f) 242.60
g) 246.20
h) 300.20
i) 23.90
j) 264.20

II.
a) 25.00
b) 29.44
c) 52.78
d) 59.44
e) 32.22

f) −5.00
g) −11.67
h) 65.00
i) −13.89
j) 0.56

7 SOME CLOSING WORDS ON MEASUREMENTS

The Eleventh General Conference on Weights and Measures, of which the United States is a signatory, adopted the Système International d'Unités (SI) in 1960. The SI is a complete system of units which incorporates the entire metric system of weights and measurements plus units for time, power, force, work, electricity, and other measurable physical quantities. Many of these units are in common usage in the U.S. presently, particularly in the scientific fields.

In 1963, the National Bureau of Standards adopted the SI for its research work and publications except for isolated exceptions. A year later the National Aeronautics and Space Administration (NASA) recommended that all formal reports utilize SI. The number of organizations utilizing the SI is constantly increasing.

Time

In SI measurement, the basic unit of time is unchanged from what we are accustomed to. The second is the basic unit of time in SI. With this basic unit, as with all basic units in SI, a derived unit is developed when two or more basic units are combined. For instance, the relationship between time and distance is sometimes referred to as speed (or velocity) and the derived unit of speed in SI is "meters per second" or m/s. The derived unit with which we are familiar is miles per hour, but the meters per second is the international unit.

The relationship between oscillation and time we call frequency (cycles per second) and the derived unit in SI is the hertz. We see this unit, actually a million times this unit (megahertz), on our FM radio dials referring to the FM frequency. The derived unit for acceleration in SI is meter per second per second or meter per second squared (m/s^2).

ELECTRICITY

For electrical current, the basic unit is the ampere which we usually call "amps". Voltage and resistance are still related by Ohm's law for volts, amperes, and ohms:

Voltage = Current (amperes) × Resistance (ohms).

Other derived electrical units in SI include the coulomb for electric charge, volt/meter for electric field strength, ohm for resistance, farad for capacitance, weber for magnetic flux, henry for inductance, tesla for magnetic flux density, and ampere per meter for magnetic field strength. The watt is the derived unit for power regardless of the source.

INTENSITY

The basic unit for luminous intensity is the candela. Lumen, candela per square meter, and lux are the derived units for luminous flux, luminance, and illumination respectively.

Other basic and derived units are included in the SI system. However, most of the other units are used almost exclusively in scientific and mathematical circles. For most of us, the change to the metric system of weights and measures will influence our daily tasks; most other changes in the SI system will go unnoticed by most of us not involved in scientific work.

APPENDIX I **U.S. WEIGHTS AND MEASURES**

Length

12 inches = 1 foot
3 feet = 1 yard
16½ feet = 1 rod
5½ yards = 1 rod
5,280 feet = 1 mile
1,760 yards = 1 mile
320 rods = 1 mile

Area

144 square inches = 1 square foot
9 square feet = 1 square yard
1296 square inches = 1 square yard
30¼ square yards = 1 square rod
160 square rods = 1 acre
640 acres = 1 section
640 acres = 1 square mile

Volume

1728 cubic inches = 1 cubic foot
27 cubic feet = 1 cubic yard

Liquid Measure

2 cups = 1 pint
2 pints = 1 quart
8 pints = 1 gallon
4 quarts = 1 gallon
31½ gallons = 1 barrel

Dry Measure

2 pints = 1 quart
8 quarts = 1 peck
4 pecks = 1 bushel

Troy Weight

24 grains = 1 pennyweight
20 pennyweights = 1 ounce
12 ounces = 1 pound

Avoirdupois Weight

7,000 grains = 1 pound
16 ounces = 1 pound
2,000 pounds = 1 ton
2,240 pounds = 1 long ton

Apothecaries' Weight

20 grains = 1 scruple
3 scruples = 1 dram
8 drams = 1 ounce
12 ounces = 1 pound

Apothecaries' Liquid Measure

60 minims = 1 fluid dram
1 drop = 1 minim
8 fluid drams = 1 fluid ounce
16 fluid ounces = 1 pint
8 pints = 1 gallon

Surveyors' Length

7.9 inches = 1 link
25 links = 1 rod
4 rods = 1 chain
80 chains = 1 mile

Surveyors' Area

625 square links = 1 square rod
16 square rods = 1 square chain
10 square chains = 1 acre
640 acres = 1 section
36 sections = 1 township

Maritime Measurement

6 feet = 1 fathom
120 fathoms = 1 cable length
7½ cable lengths = 1 mile
1 nautical mile = 6,080.2 feet
3 nautical miles = 1 league
1 knot = 1 nautical mile per hour
1 capacity ton = 100 cubic feet
1 displacement ton = 35 cubic feet
1 freight ton = 40 cubic feet

APPENDIX II **COMMON METRIC PREFIXES AND DESCRIPTION**

Prefix		Meaning
milli	1/1000	or .001 or one-thousandth basic unit
centi	1/100	or .01 or one-hundredths basic unit
deci	1/10	or .1 or one-tenth basic unit
		(one basic unit)
deka (deca)	10	or ten times the basic unit
hecto	100	or one hundred times the basic unit
kilo	1000	or one thousand times the basic unit

APPENDIX III **ENGLISH-METRIC CONVERSION GRAPHS**